Illuminate
Publishing

WJEC
AS Mathematics
Statistics 1 (S1)

Study and Revision Guide

Stephen Doyle
edited by Howard Thomas

Published in 2013 by Illuminate Publishing Ltd, P.O. Box 1160, Cheltenham, Gloucestershire GL50 9RW

Orders: Please visit www.illuminatepublishing.com
or email sales@illuminatepublishing.com

British Library Cataloguing in Publication Data

A catalogue record for this book is available from the British Library

ISBN 978-1-908682-17-8

Printed in England by 4edge, Hockley, Essex
03.14

The publisher's policy is to use papers that are natural, renewable and recyclable products made from wood grown in sustainable forests. The logging and manufacturing processes are expected to conform to the environmental regulations of the country of origin.

This material has been endorsed by WJEC and offers high quality support for the delivery of WJEC qualifications. While this material has been through a WJEC quality assurance process, all responsibility for the content remains with the publisher.

Editor: Geoff Tuttle
Cover and text design: Nigel Harriss
Text and layout: GreenGate Publishing Services, Tonbridge, Kent

Acknowledgements

I am very grateful to Rick, Geoff and the team at Illuminate Publishing for their professionalism, support and guidance throughout this project. It has been a pleasure to work so closely with them.

The author and publisher wish to thank:

Dr Howard Thomas and Paul Brown for their thorough review of the book and expert insights and observations.

Contents

How to use this book   4

Knowledge and Understanding

S1 Statistics 1   **6**

Topic 1 Probability   8

Topic 2 Discrete probability distributions   35

Topic 3 Binomial and Poisson distributions   48

Topic 4 Continuous probability distributions   64

Test yourself answers   **84**

Appendix

Use of *Statistical Tables* by Murdoch and Barnes   90

How to use this book

The contents of this study and revision guide are designed to guide you through to success in the Statistics S1 component of the WJEC Mathematics AS level examination. It has been written by an experienced author and teacher and edited by a senior subject expert. This book has been written specifically for the WJEC AS course you are taking and includes everything you need to know to perform well in your exams.

Knowledge and Understanding

Topics start with a short list of the material covered in the topic and each topic will give the underpinning knowledge and skills you need to perform well in your exams.

If any formulae are included in a topic, you will be told whether you need to remember them or whether they will be given in the formula booklet.

Formulae used will be highlighted and will be included in a Topic summary at the end of each topic.

The knowledge section is kept fairly short, leaving plenty of space for detailed explanation of examples. Pointers will be given to the theory, examples and questions that will help you understand the thinking behind the steps. You will also be given detailed advice when it is needed.

Grade boosts are tips to help you achieve your best grade by avoiding certain pitfalls which can let students down.

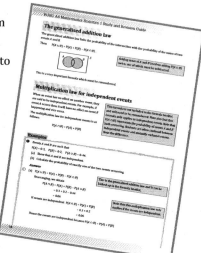

Exam Practice and Technique

Helping you understand how to answer examination questions lies at the heart of this book. This means that we have included questions throughout the book that will build up your skills and knowledge until you are at a stage to answer full exam questions on your own. Examples are included; some of which are based on recent examination questions. These are annotated with pointers and general advice about the knowledge, skills and techniques needed to answer them. There is a comprehensive Q&A section in each topic that provides actual examination questions with commentary so you can see how the question should be answered.

There is a Test yourself section where you are encouraged to answer questions on the topic and then compare your answers with the ones given at the back of the book. You should of course work through complete examination papers as part of your revision process.

We advise that you look at the WJEC website www.wjec.co.uk where you can download materials such as the specification and past papers to help you with your studies. From this website you will be able to download the formula booklet that you will use in your examinations. You will also find specimen papers and mark schemes on the site.

Good luck with your revision.

Stephen Doyle

Howard Thomas

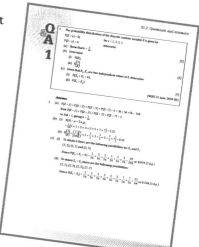

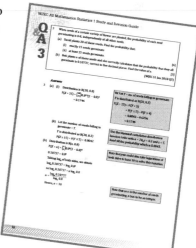

Unit S1 Statistics 1

Unit S1 covers Statistics and will involve some of the mathematics covered during your GCSE course. You must be proficient in the use of mathematical theories and techniques such as solving simple equations, transposing formulae, algebraic manipulation, solving simultaneous equations, etc., and this may require you looking back over your GCSE work.

In this unit, you may also be required to use some of the mathematical theories and techniques from units C1 and C2.

The knowledge, skills and understanding of the material in S1 will be built on in the other optional statistics units you may take.

Revision checklist

Tick column 1 when you have completed all the notes.
Tick column 2 when you think you have a good grasp of the topic.
Tick column 3 during the final revision when you feel you have mastery of the topic.

Unit S1 Statistics 1			1	2	3	Notes
	p8	Random experiments				
	p8	The use of sample space				
	p9	Events				
	p10	Venn diagrams				
	p12	Probability and outcomes				
	p13	The addition law for mutually exclusive events				
	p14	The generalised addition law				
Topic 1 Probability	p14	Multiplication law for independent events				
	p18	Multiplication law for dependent events				
	p18	Tree diagrams				
	p19	The law of total probability				
	p19	Bayes' theorem				
	p21	Probabilities for samples drawn with replacement and without replacement				
	p25	Permutations and combinations				
	p25	Using combinations to work out probabilities				
	p35	Discrete probability distributions				
	p36	Mean/expectation				
Topic 2 Discrete probability distributions	p36	The expected value of a function				
	p37	Standard deviation and variance				
	p40	Use of the results $E(aX + b) = aE(X) + b$ and $\mathrm{Var}(aX + b) = a^2\mathrm{Var}(X)$				

Topic 3 Binomial and Poisson distributions	p48	Bernoulli trials
	p48	Binomial distribution
	p50	The mean and variance of binomial distribution
	p51	Using binomial distribution tables to determine probabilities
	p53	The Poisson distribution
	p54	Mean and variance of the Poisson distribution
	p55	Using the Poisson distribution to approximate the binomial distribution
	p55	Using Poisson distribution function tables to work out $P(X \leq x)$
Topic 4 Continuous probability distributions	p64	Continuous probability distributions
	p64	The probability density function
	p66	Expected value of a continuous random variable
	p67	Variance and standard deviation for a continuous random variable
	p69	The cumulative distribution function
	p69	Obtaining the cumulative distribution function $F(x)$ from the probability density function $f(x)$
	p70	Obtaining the probability density function $f(x)$ from the cumulative distribution function $F(x)$
	p71	Medians, quartiles and percentiles
	p72	Use of the results $E(aX + b) = aE(X) + b$ and $\text{Var}(aX + b) = a^2\text{Var}(X)$
	p73	Expected value of a function of a continuous random variable

Topic 1 — Probability

This topic covers the following:

- Random experiments
- The use of sample space
- Events
- Venn diagrams
- Probability and outcomes
- The addition law for mutually exclusive events
- The generalised addition law
- Multiplication law for independent events
- Multiplication law for dependent events
- The law of total probability and Bayes' theorem
- Probabilities for samples drawn with replacement and without replacement

Random experiments

A random experiment is an experiment, trial, or observation that can be repeated numerous times under the same conditions. The outcome of an individual random experiment must in no way be affected by any previous outcome and cannot be predicted with certainty.

Examples of random experiments include:

- The tossing of a coin. The experiment can yield two possible outcomes, heads or tails.
- The roll of a die. The experiment can yield six possible outcomes and these outcomes are the numbers 1 to 6 as the die faces are labelled.
- The selection of a numbered ball (1–50) in a bag. The experiment can yield 50 possible outcomes.

The use of sample space

A complete list of all possible outcomes of a random experiment is called the **sample space** and is denoted by S.

If a single dice is thrown then there are 6 possible scores, so the sample space is

$$S = \{1, 2, 3, 4, 5, 6\}$$

If two dice are thrown then there are 36 possibilities and the sample space can be written as follows:

$$S = \begin{pmatrix} 1,1 & 1,2 & 1,3 & 1,4 & 1,5 & 1,6 \\ 2,1 & 2,2 & 2,3 & 2,4 & 2,5 & 2,6 \\ 3,1 & 3,2 & 3,3 & 3,4 & 3,5 & 3,6 \\ 4,1 & 4,2 & 4,3 & 4,4 & 4,5 & 4,6 \\ 5,1 & 5,2 & 5,3 & 5,4 & 5,5 & 5,6 \\ 6,1 & 6,2 & 6,3 & 6,4 & 6,5 & 6,6 \end{pmatrix}$$

> You can draw the sample space without the curly brackets but you should put each pair of values in brackets so the first line could be written like this:
>
> (1,1) (1,2) (1,3) (1,4) (1,5) (1,6)

Events

An event is a property associated with the outcomes of a random experiment. It is represented by a subset of the sample space.

Example 1

A cubical die is thrown once. Possible events are:

(a) A, the score obtained is an odd number

(b) B, the score obtained is greater than 4.

Sample space = set of possible outcomes

$$= \{1, 2, 3, 4, 5, 6\}$$

(a) $A = \{1, 3, 5\}$

(b) $B = \{5, 6\}$

Example 2

A card is selected from a pack of playing cards and the suit is noted. Possible events are:

(a) A, a heart will be selected

(b) B, a red card will be drawn

(c) C, a black card will be drawn.

Sample space = {heart, diamond, spade, club}

(a) A = {heart}

(b) B = {heart, diamond}

(c) C = {spade, club}

The complement of an event

The complement of an event is denoted by A', being the event that A does not occur.

In Example 1,

$S = \{1, 2, 3, 4, 5, 6\}$

$A = \{1, 3, 5\}$

and $A' = \{2, 4, 6\}$

> Elements in S but not in A.

In Example 2,

S = {heart, diamond, spade, club}

B = {heart, diamond}

and B' = {spade, club}

> Elements in S but not in B.

Combined events

For two events A and B, the event that A or B or both occur is called the union of A and B and is written $A \cup B$.

The event that both A and B occur is called the intersection of A and B and is written as $A \cap B$.

In Example 1, $A = \{1, 3, 5\}$, $B = \{5, 6\}$

and $A \cup B = \{1, 3, 5, 6\}$

and $A \cap B = \{5\}$

In Example 2, $A = \{\text{heart}\}$, $B = \{\text{heart, diamond}\}$, $C = \{\text{spade, club}\}$,

and $A \cup C = \{\text{heart, spade, club}\}$

and $A \cap B = \{\text{heart}\}$

Venn diagrams

The diagram below shows a Venn diagram. The rectangle shown below, represents the sample space S and inside this are two events A and B represented by circles.

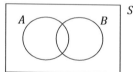

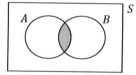

The shaded region represents the event where both A and B occur and is $A \cap B$.

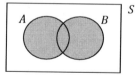

This shaded region represents the event that A or B or both A and B occur and is $A \cup B$.

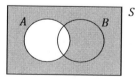

On the Venn diagram, A' is shown by the shading of the region which is not in A.

It is important to be able to describe regions using symbols and vice versa.

Examples

❶ Describe the shaded region using symbols for each of the following Venn diagrams:

(a)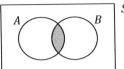

(b)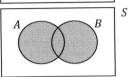

(c)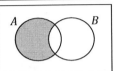

(d)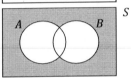

Answer

① (a) $A \cap B$

(b) $A \cup B$

(c) $A \cap B'$

(d) $(A \cup B)'$

❷ Draw Venn diagrams with events A and B and shade in the regions represented by each of the following:

(a) B'

(b) $A' \cap B$

(c) $A' \cap B'$

Answer

② (a)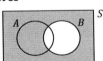

(b)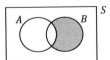

(c)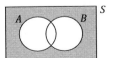

Probability and outcomes

Associated with an outcome (or event) of a random experiment is a measure of the certainty with which it can occur. This measure is known as the probability of the outcome (event). There are two ways in which probability is defined.

Equally likely outcomes

In some random experiments, it appears that any outcome is no more likely to occur than any other. In such a case, if there are N equally likely outcomes and r outcomes favour the event A, then

$$\text{Probability } (A \text{ occurs}) = \frac{r}{N}$$

> For any outcome, $r = 1$
> $$\text{Prob (outcome)} = \frac{1}{N}$$

Example

When a card is drawn from a well-shuffled pack of 52 playing cards, the probability an ace is drawn $= \dfrac{4}{52}$

> 4 aces in a pack of 52 possible outcomes.

Non-equally likely outcomes (relative frequency method)

Sometimes it cannot be assumed that outcomes are equally likely. In such a case it is supposed that a large number of trials N of the random experiment are performed and the event A occurs $r(A)$ times.

Then we take

$$\text{estimate of probability } (A \text{ occurs}) = \frac{r(A)}{N}$$

Thus, for example, if a damaged cubic die is thrown 1960 times and a score of greater than 4 is obtained 256 times we

$$\text{estimate probability (score} > 4) = \frac{256}{1960} = 0.13 \text{ (correct to 2 d.p.)}$$

Whichever method is used to define probability, we are able to define some rules to enable us to solve problems. Before doing so, we note if we regard the complete sample space as an event, then $P(S) = 1$. Similarly, for an event that cannot occur, i.e. is not contained in the sample space, the probability is zero.

We use Venn diagrams to establish the laws of probability, it being understood that the area enclosed by the circle for A is the probability of A occurring.

> Similarly for circle B.

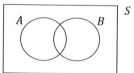

P(A')

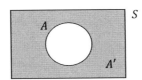

Since   P(S) = 1

         P(A') = 1 – P(A)

The addition law for mutually exclusive events

If events A and B are mutually exclusive, it means that event A can happen or event B can happen but they cannot both happen. On the Venn diagram, you can see that there is no intersection between A and B.

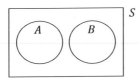

If you want the probability of A or B happening, you simply add the probability of A occurring to the probability of B occurring. This can be written as follows:

    P(A ∪ B) = P(A) + P(B)

> This formula only applies to mutually exclusive events and is not included in the formula booklet and needs to be remembered. Note that this can be used to prove that two events A and B are mutually exclusive.

Example

❶ Two events A and B are such that

    P(A) = 0.35, P(B) = 0.45 and P(A' ∩ B') = 0.6

Determine whether events A and B are mutually exclusive.

Answer

 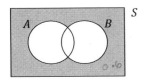

> One way to solve this is by drawing a Venn diagram for non mutually exclusive events. Note that if the events were mutually exclusive there would be no overlap between events A and B. The shaded region shows A' ∩ B' (i.e. everything that is neither A nor B). You can see that the region not shaded represents A ∪ B. Remember that the total probability of the sample space S is 1.

    P(A ∪ B) = 1 – P(A' ∩ B') = 1 – 0.6 = 0.4

Now if the events were mutually exclusive we can write

    P(A ∪ B) = P(A) + P(B) = 0.35 + 0.45 = 0.8

As these two results do not agree, the two events are not mutually exclusive.

The generalised addition law

The generalised addition law links the probability of the intersection with the probability of the union of two events A and B.

Then $P(A \cup B) = P(A) + P(B) - P(A \cap B)$.

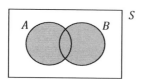

Adding areas of A and B involves adding $P(A \cap B)$ twice, one of which must be subtracted.

This is a very important formula which must be remembered.

Multiplication law for independent events

When an event has no effect on another event, they are said to be independent events. For example, if event A occurs then it will have no effect on event B happening and vice versa.

The multiplication law for independent events is as follows:

$$P(A \cap B) = P(A) \times P(B)$$

This formula is not included in the formula booklet and will need to be remembered. Note also that this formula only applies to independent events. Note that $P(A \cap B)$ represents the probability of events A and B both occurring. Students are often confused between independent events and mutually exclusive events. Note the difference.

Examples

❶   Events A and B are such that

$P(A) = 0 \cdot 3$, $P(B) = 0 \cdot 2$, $P(A \cup B) = 0 \cdot 44$.

(a)   Show that A and B are independent.

(b)   Calculate the probability of exactly one of the two events occurring.

Answer

①   (a) $P(A \cup B) = P(A) + P(B) - P(A \cap B)$

This is the generalised addition law and it can be looked up in the formula booklet.

Rearranging, we obtain

$P(A \cap B) = P(A) + P(B) - P(A \cup B)$

$= 0.3 + 0.2 - 0.44$

$= 0.06$

Note that this multiplication law only applies if the events are independent.

If events are independent $P(A \cap B) = P(A) \times P(B)$

$= 0.3 \times 0.2$

$= 0.06$

Hence the events are independent because $P(A \cap B) = P(A) \times P(B)$

(b) Probability of exactly one event = P($A \cup B$) – P($A \cap B$) = 0.44 – 0.06 = 0.38

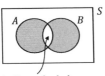

$A \cap B$ not shaded

Another way to work this out is as follows:

P(A only) = 0.3 – 0.06 = 0.24

P(B only) = 0.2 – 0.06 = 0.14

P(A or B only) = 0.24 + 0.14 = 0.38

Alternative answer

This problem could also be solved as follows:

① (a)

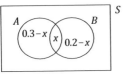

Grade boost

There are often several ways of solving the same problem. Many people find a visual method of solving a problem like this easier. Probability questions can often be solved using diagrams such as Venn diagrams and tree diagrams. Choose the method you find easiest.

Let x = P($A \cap B$) so the probability of A only is 0.3 – x and the probability of B only is 0.2 – x.

From the question, P($A \cup B$) = 0.44, so from the Venn diagram we have

$$0.3 - x + x + 0.2 - x = 0.44$$

$$0.5 - x = 0.44$$

Hence $x = 0.06$

If the two events A and B are independent, then

$$P(A \cap B) = P(A) \times P(B) = 0.3 \times 0.2 = 0.06$$

As P($A \cap B$) = 0.06 and P(A) × P(B) = 0.06, we have P($A \cap B$) = P(A) × P(B) which proves that events A and B are independent.

(b) Probability of exactly one of the two events occurring is the shaded area shown.

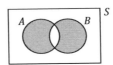

P(exactly one of the events occurring) = 0.3 – x + 0.2 – x = 0.5 – 2x

As x = 0.06, required probability = 0.5 – 0.12 = 0.38

❷ The independent events A and B are such that

P(A) = 0·6,   P(B) = 0·3.

Find the value of

(a) P($A \cup B$)   [3]

(b) P($A \cup B'$)   [3]

(WJEC S1 June 2010 Q1)

Answer

② (a) Using $P(A \cup B) = P(A) + P(B) - P(A \cap B)$, we obtain

$P(A \cup B) = 0.6 + 0.3 - (0.6 \times 0.3) = 0.72$

> Note that $P(A \cap B) = P(A) \times P(B)$
> $= 0.6 \times 0.3 = 0.18$

(b) $P(B') = 1 - P(B) = 1 - 0.3 = 0.7$

Now, $P(A \cup B') = P(A) + P(B') - P(A \cap B')$

$= P(A) + P(B') - P(A) \times P(B')$

$= 0.6 + 0.7 - 0.6 \times 0.7$

$= 0.88$

> Note you can use the result
> $$P(A \cup B) = P(A) + P(B) - P(A \cap B)$$
> but replacing the occurrences of B with B' to obtain the following:
> $$P(A \cup B') = P(A) + P(B') - P(A \cap B')$$
> Note A and B are independent.

Alternative method

② (a) As the events are independent $P(A \cap B) = P(A) \times P(B)$

$= 0.6 \times 0.3 = 0.18$

> This part could also be solved by drawing a Venn diagram.

$P(A \text{ only}) = 0.6 - 0.18 = 0.42$

$P(B \text{ only}) = 0.3 - 0.18 = 0.12$

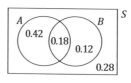

$P(A \cup B) = 0.42 + 0.18 + 0.12 = 0.72.$

$P(A \cup B)' = 1 - 0.72 = 0.28$

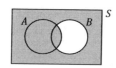

> The Venn diagram is drawn with the shaded region representing $A \cup B'$.
> It is then easy to spot that if you subtract the probability of event B only from 1, you obtain the required probability.

$P(A \cup B') = 1 - P(B \text{ only occurs}) = 1 - 0.12 = 0.88$

❸ A and B are two events such that

$P(A) = 0.35$, $P(B) = 0.25$ and $P(A \cup B) = 0.5$. Find

(a) $P(A \cap B)$

(b) $P(A')$

(c) $P(A \cup B')$

Answer

③ (a) $P(A \cap B) = P(A) + P(B) - P(A \cup B)$

$= 0.35 + 0.25 - 0.5$

$= 0.1$

> Rearrange $P(A \cup B) = P(A) + P(B) - P(A \cap B)$

(b) $P(A') = 1 - P(A) = 1 - 0.35 = 0.65$

(c)

$$P(B') = 1 - P(B) = 1 - 0.25 = 0.75$$

$$P(A \cup B') = P(A) + P(B') - P(A \cap B') = 0.35 + 0.75 - 0.25 = 0.85$$

4 The events A and B are such that $P(A) = P(B) = p$ and $P(A \cup B) = 0.64$.

(a) Given that A and B are mutually exclusive, find the value of p. [2]

(b) Given, instead, that A and B are independent, show that

$$25p^2 - 50p + k = 0,$$

where k is a constant whose value should be found.

Hence find the value of p. [5]

(WJEC S1 Jan 2011 Q2)

Answer

④ (a) $p + p = 0.64$

$2p = 0.64$

$p = 0.32$

> As A and B are mutually exclusive there is no overlap between events A and B. Hence $P(A \cup B)$ is simply the probability of A or B occurring so the probabilities for each of these events are added.

(b) (i) $P(A \cap B) = p \times p = p^2$

Using $P(A \cup B) = P(A) + P(B) - P(A \cap B)$, we obtain

$$0.64 = 2p - p^2$$

$$p^2 - 2p + 0.64 = 0$$

> As events A and B are now independent, there may be an overlap between the two events, so $A \cap B$ could exist.

Multiplying the above equation through by 25, we obtain

$$25p^2 - 50p + 16 = 0$$

Comparing this equation with the one given in the question, we obtain $k = 16$

Factorising $25p^2 - 50p + 16 = 0$, we obtain

$$(5p - 2)(5p - 8) = 0$$

$$\text{So } p = \frac{2}{5} \text{ or } \frac{8}{5}$$

> This is a quadratic equation that can be solved by factorising, completing the square or using the formula.

However, as p is a probability, it cannot be greater than 1, so the answer $p = \frac{8}{5}$ is disregarded.

Hence, $p = \frac{2}{5}$ (or 0.4 as a decimal).

⋙ Grade boost

When you solve a quadratic you often get two different answers. When this happens always ask yourself if both or just one of the answers is allowable.

Multiplication law for dependent events

The probability of an event B occurring can depend on whether or not an event A has occurred before it. The conditional probability of B given A occurs is written as $P(B|A)$.

There is a law used when dealing with dependent events called the multiplication law for dependent events. The multiplication law for dependent events is

$$P(A \cap B) = P(A)P(B|A)$$

and also, $P(A \cap B) = P(B)P(A|B)$

> Note that this formula is included in the formula booklet and need not be remembered.

> This is not included in the formula booklet. Notice the way the A and B are swapped around on the right-hand side of the formula.

Tree diagrams

Tree diagrams are diagrams used to represent the probabilities of combined events. Each path (which is a branch of the tree) corresponds to a certain sequence of events. By multiplying the probabilities of the separate events along the path, you can work out the probability of a particular sequence of events. If the required probability involves several paths, the probabilities of each path are found and then added together to give the required probability.

Example 1

❶ In a certain country, 80% of the defendants being tried in the law courts actually committed the crime. For those who committed the crime, the probability of being found guilty is 0·9. For those who did not commit the crime, the probability of being found guilty is 0·05.

(a) Find the probability that a randomly chosen defendant is found guilty.   [3]

(b) Given that a randomly chosen defendant is found guilty, find the probability that this defendant committed the crime.   [3]

(WJEC S1 Jan 2011 Q6)

Answer

① (a) There are two ways in which the defendant could be found guilty.

He/she could have committed the crime and be found guilty.

He/she could have not committed the crime and be found guilty.

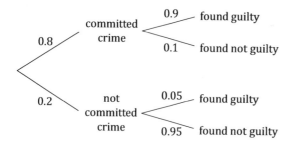

> A tree diagram is drawn. Notice that the first event is whether the person committed the crime or not and the second event is whether they were subsequently found guilty or not.

> There are two paths that will find the person guilty. The probability of each path is found and the required probability is the sum of these.

Hence, probability found guilty =

P(committed crime) × P(found guilty) + P(not committed crime) × P(found guilty)

= 0.8 × 0.9 + 0.2 × 0.05 = 0.73

(b) Let event A be that he/she committed the crime.

Let event B be that he/she were found guilty.

$$P(A \cap B) = P(B)P(A|B)$$

$$P(A|B) = \frac{P(A \cap B)}{P(B)} = \frac{0.8 \times 0.9}{0.73} = \frac{72}{73}$$

> Note that $P(A \cap B)$ is the probability that they committed the crime and are found guilty. $P(B)$ is the probability that they are found guilty.

The law of total probability

If $A_1, A_2, ... , A_n$ are mutually exclusive and exhaustive events, then

$$A_1 \cup A_2 \cup A_3 \cup ... \cup A_n = S$$

and every possible outcome is contained in one and only one of the A events.

If B is another event,

$$B = (A_1 \cap B) \cup (A_2 \cap B) \cup (A_3 \cap B) ... \cup (A_n \cap B)$$

> B occurs with A_1, or with A_2, etc.

and

$$P(B) = P(A_1 \cap B) + P(A_2 \cap B) + ... + P(A_n \cap B)$$

$$= P(A_1)P(B|A_1) + P(A_2)P(B|A_2) + ... + P(A_n)P(B|A_n)$$

$$= \sum P(A_j)P(B|A_j)$$

This formula is called the law of total probability.

The law of total probability is used when adding the probabilities of each possible path in a tree diagram.

Bayes' theorem

Bayes' theorem gives us a way of calculating $P(A|B)$ from a knowledge of $P(B|A)$.

If $A_1, A_2, A_3, ... , A_n$ are mutually exclusive events that form the same space S, and B is any event from the same sample space such that $P(B) > 0$, then Bayes' theorem states:

$$P(A_j|B) = \frac{P(A_j)}{P(B)}$$

$$= \frac{P(A_j)P(B|A_j)}{\sum P(A_i)P(B|A_i)}$$

> This formula is included in the formula booklet so it need not be remembered.

Examples

❶ Three bags contain black and white balls. Bag 1 contains 5 black balls and 5 white balls, Bag 2 contains 7 black and 3 white balls and Bag 3 contains 6 black balls and 4 white balls.

A bag is chosen and a ball is randomly chosen from that bag.

The probability of choosing Bag 1 is $\frac{1}{3}$, the probability of choosing Bag 2 is $\frac{1}{2}$ and the probability of choosing Bag 3 is $\frac{1}{6}$.

Calculate the probability that the selected ball is white.

Answer

① Let set A_1 be the event that Bag 1 is chosen, A_2 be the event that Bag 2 is chosen and A_3 be the event that Bag 3 is chosen. Also, let W be the event that a white ball is drawn.

Now $P(W) = P(A_1)P(W|A_1) + P(A_2)P(W|A_2) + P(A_3)P(W|A_3)$

Now $P(A_1) = \frac{1}{3}$, $P(A_2) = \frac{1}{2}$, $P(A_3) = \frac{1}{6}$

and $P(W|A_1) = \frac{5}{10}$, $P(W|A_2) = \frac{3}{10}$, $P(W|A_3) = \frac{4}{10}$

Then $P(W) = \dfrac{1}{3} \times \dfrac{5}{10} + \dfrac{1}{2} \times \dfrac{3}{10} + \dfrac{1}{6} \times \dfrac{4}{10} = \dfrac{23}{60}$

❷ Jack is taking part in a quiz programme. For each question in the quiz, four answer options are given, only one of which is correct. Jack has probability 0.6 of knowing the correct answer to a question, and when he does not know the correct answer he chooses one of the four answers at random.

(a) Calculate the probability that Jack gives the correct answer to a question. [3]

(b) Given that Jack gave the correct answer to a question, find the probability that he knew the correct answer. [3]

(WJEC S1 June 2010 Q5)

Answer

② (a)

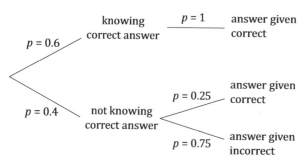

P(giving correct answer) = (0.6 × 1) + (0.4 × 0.25)

= 0.7

> It is always advisable to draw a tree diagram unless the number of branches makes it too difficult to draw.

> Notice that once Jack knows the correct answer, the probability then of him giving the correct answer is 1.

> There are two paths to consider on the tree diagram.

(b) Probability (knew correct answer/gave the correct answer)

$$= \frac{\text{Prob (knew correct answer and gave correct answer)}}{\text{Prob (gave correct answer)}}$$

$$= \frac{0.6}{0.7} = 0.857 \text{ (correct to 3 d.p.)}$$

❸ Two bags 1 and 2 contain black and white balls. Bag 1 contains 5 black and 5 white balls. Bag 2 contains 2 black balls and 6 white balls.

A bag is selected at random and a ball is randomly drawn from that bag. If the drawn ball is black, what is the probability that Bag 2 was selected?

Answer

③ Let A_1 be the event that Bag 1 was selected.

Let A_2 be the event that Bag 2 was selected.

Let B be the event that a black ball was drawn.

Then $\qquad P(A_1) = \frac{1}{2}, P(A_2) = \frac{1}{2}$

$P(B|A_1) = \frac{5}{10}, P(B|A_2) = \frac{2}{8}$

Then $\qquad P(B) = P(A_1)P(B|A_1) + P(A_2)P(B|A_2)$

$$= \frac{1}{2} \times \frac{5}{10} + \frac{1}{2} \times \frac{2}{8} = \frac{3}{8}$$

$$P(A_2|B) = \frac{P(A_2)P(B|A_2)}{P(B)} = \frac{\frac{1}{2} \times \frac{2}{8}}{\frac{3}{8}} = \frac{1}{3}$$

Probabilities for samples drawn with replacement and without replacement

It is important to consider whether replacement takes place or not with each problem. For example, if two counters are taken out from a bag consisting of 3 red and 7 blue counters with replacement, then when the second counter is taken from the back the bag still contains 3 red and 7 blue counters. If, however, replacement does not take place and a red counter is removed first, the number of red counters in the bag is reduced by one and the total number of counters in the bag is reduced by one.

Examples

❶ There are 3 red and 7 blue counters in a bag and two counters are picked at random from the bag.

Find the probability that:

(a) Two red counters are chosen.

(b) A red and blue counter are chosen.

Answer

① (a) The following tree diagram is drawn.

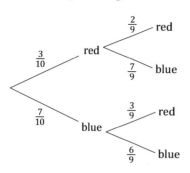

> Taking two counters together is considered the same as taking one counter and without replacing it, taking another counter.

$$P(\text{Red and red}) = \frac{3}{10} \times \frac{2}{9} = \frac{1}{15}$$

(b) P(Red and blue) = P(RB) + P(BR)

> Note that red and blue does not specify an order. There are two paths which need to be considered on the tree diagram.

$$= \frac{3}{10} \times \frac{7}{9} + \frac{7}{10} \times \frac{3}{9}$$

$$= \frac{42}{90} = \frac{7}{15}$$

> Remember to fully cancel fractions. Use your calculator to help you.

❷ A group of 10 children consists of 4 girls and 6 boys; 2 children from the group are picked at random to take part in an interview. Find the probability that:

(a) two girls are chosen,

(b) a boy and a girl are chosen.

Answer

② (a)

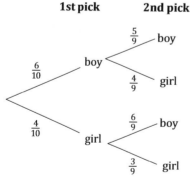

> A tree diagram is drawn showing the possible selections. The probability of a particular sequence is found by multiplying the probabilities along the branches making up the sequence.

> Remember to cancel any fractions. You are allowed to use a calculator for this paper so make sure you know how to do fractions using your calculator.

(a) Probability (2 girls chosen) $= \frac{4}{10} \times \frac{3}{9} = \frac{2}{15}$

(b) Probability (boy and girl chosen) = P(BG) + P(GB)

$$= \left(\frac{6}{10} \times \frac{4}{9}\right) + \left(\frac{4}{10} \times \frac{6}{9}\right) = \frac{8}{15}$$

❸ Amy has a bag of sweets containing toffees, mints and caramels. There are 6 toffees, 4 mints and 2 caramels. Three sweets are chosen at random from the bag. Find the probability that she chooses:

(a) one of each type

(b) all toffees

(c) all of the same type.

Answer

③ (a) Here are the ways of picking one sweet of each type:

TMC
TCM
CMT
CTM
MTC
MCT

> We discuss a quick way to find the number of arrangements in the next section.
>
> You can work the number of arrangements using the formula for a permutation. The formula is $^nP_r = \dfrac{n!}{(n-r)!}$ and here n is 3 and r is 3 so $^3P_3 = \dfrac{3!}{(3-3)!} = \dfrac{3!}{0!} = 1 \times 2 \times 3 = 6$. Remember that $0! = 1$. This will save you the time listing the arrangements.

> Note that the formula for a permutation is obtained from the formula booklet.

Probability of obtaining TMC = $\dfrac{6}{12} \times \dfrac{4}{11} \times \dfrac{2}{10} = \dfrac{48}{1320} = \dfrac{2}{55}$

Probability of obtaining TCM = $\dfrac{6}{12} \times \dfrac{2}{11} \times \dfrac{4}{10} = \dfrac{48}{1320} = \dfrac{2}{55}$

Probability of obtaining one sweet of each type = $6 \times \dfrac{2}{55} = \dfrac{12}{55}$

> Notice that the probabilities are the same and will be for all the other arrangements we are considering.
>
> As there are 6 arrangements with the same probability we just multiply the probability of one of the arrangements by 6.

(b) Probability of all toffees = $\dfrac{6}{12} \times \dfrac{5}{11} \times \dfrac{4}{10} = \dfrac{120}{1320} = \dfrac{1}{11}$

(c) Probability of all mints = $\dfrac{4}{12} \times \dfrac{3}{11} \times \dfrac{2}{10} = \dfrac{24}{1320} = \dfrac{1}{55}$

> Note that as there are only 2 caramels, it is impossible to pick 3 of them.

Probability of all the same type = probability of all toffees + probability of all mints

$$= \dfrac{1}{11} + \dfrac{1}{55} = \dfrac{6}{55}$$

❹ Alan and Bill play a game with darts in which they throw a dart at the 'bull' on the dartboard alternately, starting with Alan, and the winner is the first to hit the 'bull'. Each time they throw a dart at the 'bull', Alan hits it with probability 0·2 and Bill hits it with probability 0·3. Find the probability that:

(a) Bill wins the game with his first throw [2]

(b) Bill wins the game with his second throw [2]

(c) Bill wins the game. [4]

(WJEC S1 June 2010 Q4)

Answer

④ (a)

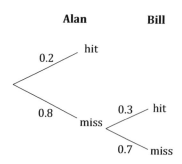

Alan   Bill

Alan has first throw so he must miss first before Bill throws a dart.	

P(Bill hits with first throw) = P(Alan misses with first throw) × P(Bill hits with first throw)

= 0.8 × 0.3 = 0.24

(b)

The tree diagram is extended to show the events up to and including Bill having his second throw.

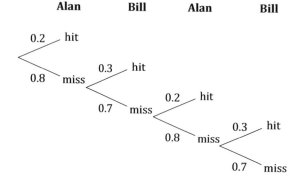

Note that Alan and Bill must miss up to Bill's second throw.

Probability Bill hits with second throw = 0.8 × 0.7 × 0.8 × 0.3 = 0.1344

(c) Probability that Bill wins = 0.24 + 0.24 × 0.56 + 0.24 × 0.56² + ...

$$S_\infty = \frac{a}{1-r}$$

$$S_\infty = \frac{0.24}{1-0.56} = 0.5455$$

Hence, probability that Bill wins = 0.5455 or 0.55 (correct to two decimal places).

You have to spot that the above is a geometric series as it is in the form: $a + ar + ar^2 + ar^3 + ...$

The first term $a = 0.24$, and the common ratio $r = 0.56$. The sum to infinity formula can be used to work out the total, which is the probability that Bill wins.

The formula $S_\infty = \frac{a}{1-r}$ for the sum to infinity for a geometric series is given in the formula booklet.

Permutations and combinations

A permutation is an arrangement of things. The order of things is considered in a permutation.

A combination is a selection of things. The order has no importance in a combination.

The number of arrangements when r objects are chosen from n is given by $^nP_r = \dfrac{n!}{(n-r)!}$

This is the formula for a permutation.

> Remember that the order is considered in a permutation.

The number of selections when r objects are chosen from n is given by

$^nC_r = \dfrac{n!}{(n-r)!\,r!}$

This is the formula for a combination.

> Remember that the order is **not** considered in a combination.

Using combinations to work out probabilities

You can use combinations to work out probabilities. In this section we will be looking at how this is done. Many of the questions involving the selection of certain items can be solved using combinations. The questions can usually also be solved by using tree diagrams. You are free to choose which method you prefer.

Suppose there are 9 sweets in a bag: 3 blue, 2 red and 4 yellow; 3 sweets are chosen at random without replacement and we want to find the probability of obtaining 3 yellow sweets.

There are two things we need to find.

Firstly, we need the number of ways 3 objects (i.e. sweets) are chosen from 9. This can be found by determining $^9C_3$.

$^9C_3 = 84$ (this value is found by using the ^nC_r button on your calculator).

Secondly, we need to find the number of ways 3 yellow sweets can be chosen from 4 yellow sweets by determining $^4C_3$.

$$^4C_3 = 4$$

Probability of obtaining 3 yellow sweets $= \dfrac{^4C_3}{^9C_3} = \dfrac{1}{21}$

> Notice that this is the number of ways of picking 3 yellow sweets from 4 divided by the number of ways of picking 3 sweets from 9.

If we wanted to find the probability of no blue sweets being obtained when 3 sweets are selected at random, we would use the following.

Again the total number of ways 3 sweets can be chosen from 9 is $^9C_3$. The number of ways 3 sweets can be selected from the 6 that are not blue is given by $^6C_3$.

Hence, the probability of obtaining no blue sweets $= \dfrac{^6C_3}{^9C_3} = \dfrac{5}{21}$

If you require the probability of one sweet of each colour being selected you need to work out:

the number of ways one red sweet can be selected from 2 red sweets (i.e. $^2C_1$)

the number of ways one blue sweet can be selected from 3 blue sweets (i.e. $^3C_1$)

the number of ways one yellow sweet can be selected from 4 yellow sweets (i.e. $^4C_1$)

the number of ways 3 sweets can be chosen from 9 (i.e. $^9C_3$)

Hence, the probability of one sweet of each colour $= \dfrac{^2C_1 \times ^3C_1 \times ^4C_1}{^9C_3} = \dfrac{2}{7}$

Examples

❶ A bag contains 10 balls of which 1 is red, 5 are green and 4 are blue. Jack chooses 3 of the balls from the bag at random without replacement. Find the probability that:

(a) three blue balls are chosen

(b) no blue balls are chosen.

Answer

① (a) Number of ways 3 objects can be chosen from 10

$= {}^{10}C_3 = 120$

Number of ways 3 objects can be selected from 4

$= {}^4C_3 = 4$

Probability three blue balls are chosen $= \dfrac{{}^4C_3}{{}^{10}C_3}$

$$= \frac{4}{120} = \frac{1}{30}$$

(b) Probability no blue balls are chosen $= \dfrac{{}^6C_3}{{}^{10}C_3} = \dfrac{20}{120} = \dfrac{1}{6}$

Make sure you can work out combinations using your calculator. There is a formula for working out combinations but it is quicker to use your calculator.

${}^4C_3$ works out the number of ways 3 blue balls can be selected from 4 balls.

Here the choice relates to the non-blue balls, i.e. 6 balls.

❷ Jessica has 12 handbags in her handbag collection. She has 2 black, 6 silver and 4 beige handbags. Jessica goes to the drawer containing her handbags and picks three handbags at random. Find the probability of her selecting:

(a) one handbag of each colour

(b) three silver handbags

(c) three handbags of the same colour.

Important note: You could use the alternative method of using tree diagrams to answer this question.

Answer

② (a) P(one of each colour) $= \dfrac{{}^2C_1 \times {}^6C_1 \times {}^4C_1}{{}^{12}C_3}$

$$= \frac{12}{55} \text{ or } 0.2182 \text{ (correct to 4 d.p.)}$$

(b) P(three silver) $= \dfrac{{}^6C_3}{{}^{12}C_3} = \dfrac{20}{220} = \dfrac{1}{11}$ or 0.0909 (correct to 4 d.p.)

(c) P(three handbags of the same colour) $= \dfrac{{}^6C_3}{{}^{12}C_3} + \dfrac{{}^4C_3}{{}^{12}C_3} = \dfrac{6}{55}$

$$= 0.1091$$

Note that there is no chance of selecting 3 black handbags as there are only 2 in the drawer. This is the reason there are only two combinations in the numerator.

Notice the way the combinations are added in the numerator. This is because the total probability is the probability of picking 3 silver OR 3 beige handbags, noting there are only 2 black handbags.

❸   A board of directors has 4 vacancies. There are 3 men and 5 women who are suitable for the position.

(a)   Calculate the number of ways of selecting 4 people to fill the vacancies.

(b)   If the 4 vacancies are filled at random, what is the probability that there will be at least 2 women chosen?

Answer

③   (a)   Number of ways of selecting 4 people from 8 = $^8C_4 = 70$

(b)   Need to consider the following probabilities:

Number of ways of selecting 2 women and 2 men = $^5C_2 \times {}^3C_2 = 30$

Number of ways of selecting 3 women and 1 man = = $^5C_3 \times {}^3C_1 = 30$

Number of ways of selecting 4 women and 0 men = $^5C_4 \times {}^3C_0 = 5$

Hence, number of ways of selecting at least 2 women = 30 + 30 + 5 = 65

Probability of at least 2 women chosen = $\dfrac{\text{number of ways of choosing at least 2 women}}{\text{number of ways of selecting 3 people from 8}}$

$$= \frac{65}{70}$$

$$= \frac{13}{14}$$

Examination style questions

❶ A board of directors for an engineering company consist of 9 directors of which 2 are from sales, 3 are from accounts and 4 are from technical. A smaller sub-group of 3 directors is to be formed to work on a project. It is decided to choose these 3 directors at random.

Calculate the probability that this sub-group contains:

(a) no directors from sales [5]

(b) 1 director from sales, one director from accounts and one director from technical. [3]

Answer

① (a) Probability no directors from sales $= \dfrac{7}{9} \times \dfrac{6}{8} \times \dfrac{5}{7} = \dfrac{5}{12}$

Also, $\dfrac{^7C_3}{^9C_3} = \dfrac{35}{84} = \dfrac{5}{12}$

(b) Three members (one of each type of director) can be arranged in 6 ways:

Probability of TBG $= \dfrac{2}{9} \times \dfrac{3}{8} \times \dfrac{4}{7} = \dfrac{1}{21}$

Also, $\dfrac{^2C_1 \times {}^3C_1 \times {}^4C_1}{^9C_3} = \dfrac{24}{84} = \dfrac{2}{7}$

Probability of three members of each type $= 6 \times \dfrac{2}{9} \times \dfrac{3}{8} \times \dfrac{4}{7} = \dfrac{2}{7}$

Note the '6' appears here because there are 6 ways of arranging 3 members.

❷ Two independent events A and B are such that:

$P(A) = 0.4$, $P(B) = 0.3$

Find:

(a) $P(A \cap B)$ [1]

(b) $P(A \cup B)$ [3]

(c) the probability that neither A nor B occurs [3]

(d) $P(A \mid A \cup B)$. [3]

Answer

② (a) Independent means $P(A \cap B) = P(A) \times P(B) = 0.4 \times 0.3 = 0.12$

Note
$P(A \cup B)' = P(A' \cap B')$.

(b) $P(A \cup B) = P(A) + P(B) - P(A \cap B) = 0.4 + 0.3 - 0.12 = 0.58$

(c) Probability that neither A nor B occurs $= P(A \cup B)' = 1 - P(A \cup B)$

$= 1 - 0.58 = 0.42$

This could also be worked out in the following way:
$P(A' \cap B') = (1 - 0.4)(1 - 0.3) = 0.42$,
since A' and B' are independent.

(d)

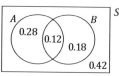

$P(A \mid A \cup B) = \dfrac{P(A)}{P(A \cup B)} = \dfrac{0.4}{0.58} = 0.69$

(correct to two decimal places)

We are asked for the probability of event A given that event $A \cup B$ has taken place. Hence we need to divide the probability of A by the probability of $A \cup B$. A Venn diagram can help present the probabilities already found.

Note that the top is
$P(A \cap (A \cup B)) = P(A)$.

Test yourself

Answer the following questions and check your answers before moving on to the next topic.

1 The events A and B are such that:

$P(A) = 0.45$, $P(B) = 0.30$, $P(A \cap B) = 0.25$

Calculate the probability of:

(a) $P(A \cup B)$

(b) $P(A' \cap B')$

(c) $P(B|A')$.

2 A bag contains 9 counters of which there are 2 red, 3 blue and 4 yellow. Three of these counters are chosen at random without replacement. Find the probability that:

(a) three yellow counters are chosen

(b) no blue counters are chosen

(c) one counter of each colour is chosen.

3 A bag contains 10 sweets of which 2 are red, 3 are blue and 5 are yellow. Adam chooses two sweets at random from the bag.

(a) Calculate the probability that these two sweets are of the same colour.

(b) Hence, or otherwise, calculate the probability that these two sweets are of different colours.

4 Amy and Bethany each throw a fair cubical die with faces numbered, 1, 2, 3, 4, 5, 6.

(a) Calculate the probability that the score on Amy's die is:

(i) equal to the score on Bethany's die

(ii) greater than the score on Bethany's die.

(b) Given that the sum of the scores on the two dice is 4, find the probability that the two scores are equal.

5 A and B are two independent events such that:

$P(A) = 0.3$ and $P(A \cup B) = 0.5$.

(a) Calculate $P(B)$.

(b) Calculate the probability that exactly one of the two events occurs.

(c) Given that exactly one of the two events occurs, calculate the probability that B occurs.

6 The events A and B are such that:

$P(A) = 0.4$, $P(B) = 0.35$ and $P(A' \cap B') = 0.4$.

Determine whether:

(a) A and B are mutually exclusive

(b) A and B are independent.

1   Jean has two fair dice, each in the shape of a regular tetrahedron. The four faces of each dice are numbered 1, 2, 3, 4 respectively. She throws the two dice simultaneously and the score on each die is defined as the number on the face in contact with the table.

(a) Write down the sample space.   [2]

(b) Calculate the probability that:

    (i)   the sum of the scores on the two dice is 6

    (ii) the scores on the two dice are consecutive integers.   [4]

(WJEC S1 Jan 2011 Q1)

Answer

1   (a) (1,1) (1,2) (1,3) (1,4)

        (2,1) (2,2) (2,3) (2,4)

        (3,1) (3,2) (3,3) (3,4)

        (4,1) (4,2) (4,3) (4,4)

> The first number in each bracketed pair represents the number on the first die when tossed and the second number is the score on the second die when tossed.

(b) (i)   Number of pairs which add up to 6 is 3

$$\text{Probability} = \frac{3}{16}$$

> The pairs which add up to 6 are: (2, 4), (3, 3) and (4, 2)

    (ii) Number of pairs with consecutive integers = 6

$$\text{Probability} = \frac{6}{16} = \frac{3}{8}$$

> Note that 'consecutive integers' means whole numbers that are next to each other. The pairs with consecutive integers are: (1,2), (2,1), (2,3), (3, 2), (3, 4) and (4,3).

2   Two events A and B are such that:

$$P(A) = 0.4, P(B) = 0.2, P(A \cup B) = 0.5$$

(a) Calculate $P(A \cap B)$.   [2]

(b) Determine whether or not A and B are independent.   [2]

(c) Calculate $P(A|B')$.   [3]

Answer

2   (a) Using $P(A \cup B) = P(A) + P(B) - P(A \cap B)$, we obtain

$$0.5 = 0.4 + 0.2 - P(A \cap B)$$

$$P(A \cap B) = 0.1$$

(b) $P(A) \times P(B) = 0.4 \times 0.2 = 0.08$

As $P(A \cap B) \neq P(A) \times P(B)$ the events A and B are not independent.

(c) $P(B') = 1 - P(B) = 1 - 0.2 = 0.8$

$$P(A \cap B') = 0.4 - 0.1 = 0.3$$

$$P(A|B') = \frac{P(A \cap B')}{P(B')} = \frac{0.3}{0.8} = 0.375$$

> $P(A) = P(A \cap B) + P(A \cap B')$
> so $P(A \cap B') = P(A) - P(A \cap B)$

3 Cyril buys a bag containing 9 sweets of which 5 are red, 3 are green and 1 is yellow. He allows Gwyneth to choose 3 sweets at random from the bag. Calculate the probability that she chooses:

(a) 1 sweet of each colour [3]

(b) no green sweets [2]

(c) 3 sweets of the same colour. [3]

(WJEC S1 June 2011 Q1)

Answer

3 (a) Here are the possible ways of obtaining one sweet of each colour:

RGY

RYG

| The number of ways of arranging 3 different items is $3! = 3 \times 2 \times 1 = 6$. |

GYR

GRY

YGR

| Notice how the number of sweets decreases by 1 each time a sweet is picked. |

YRG

Probability of obtaining RGY $= \dfrac{5}{9} \times \dfrac{3}{8} \times \dfrac{1}{7} = \dfrac{15}{504}$

Probability of obtaining RYG $= \dfrac{5}{9} \times \dfrac{1}{8} \times \dfrac{3}{7} = \dfrac{15}{504}$

| Notice that the same numbers occur as for the probability of obtaining RGY, just in a different order. This will happen for all 6 ways so we don't have to work them out separately. Instead we can multiply one of the probabilities by 6. |

Probability of obtaining one sweet of each colour

$= 6 \times \dfrac{5}{9} \times \dfrac{3}{8} \times \dfrac{1}{7} = 6 \times \dfrac{15}{504} = \dfrac{90}{504} = \dfrac{5}{28}$ (or 0.179 as a decimal)

Alternatively,

Probability $= \dfrac{{}^5C_1 \times {}^3C_1 \times {}^1C_1}{{}^9C_3} = \dfrac{5 \times 3 \times 1}{84} = \dfrac{5}{28}$

| Remember to check to see if the fraction will cancel. You can use your calculator to do this. |

(b) Probability of no green sweets $= \dfrac{6}{9} \times \dfrac{5}{8} \times \dfrac{4}{7} = \dfrac{120}{504} = \dfrac{5}{21}$ (or 0.238 as a decimal)

Alternatively,

Probability $= \dfrac{{}^6C_3}{{}^9C_3} = \dfrac{20}{84} = \dfrac{5}{21}$

| The probability of not obtaining a green sweet with the first sweet is 6 out of 9 (i.e. there are 6 sweets that aren't green). For the second it is 5 out of 8. This is because the number of not green sweets has been reduced by the one already picked. Also the number of sweets has been reduced by one. For the third selection the probability is 4 out of 7. |

(c) P(All red) $= \dfrac{5}{9} \times \dfrac{4}{8} \times \dfrac{3}{7} = \dfrac{5}{42}$

P(All green) $= \dfrac{3}{9} \times \dfrac{2}{8} \times \dfrac{1}{7} = \dfrac{1}{84}$

P(Same colour) $= \dfrac{5}{42} + \dfrac{1}{84} = \dfrac{11}{84}$

| The selection is restricted to the red and green sweets, 6 in all. |

Or Probability $= \dfrac{{}^5C_3 + {}^3C_3}{{}^9C_3} = \dfrac{10 + 1}{84} = \dfrac{11}{84}$

| Note that there is only one yellow sweet so you cannot get 3 yellow sweets. |

| Remember to cancel fractions as far as possible before giving them as your final answer. Also remember that you can add fractions using your calculator. |

4 Events *A* and *B* are such that

$P(A) = 0.2$, $P(B) = 0.4$, $P(A \cup B) = 0.52$.

(a) Show that *A* and *B* are independent. [5]

(b) Calculate the probability of exactly one of the two events occurring. [2]

(c) Given that exactly one of the two events occurs, calculate the probability that A occurs. [3]

(WJEC S1 Jan 2010 Q2)

Answer

4 (a) Using $P(A \cup B) = P(A) + P(B) - P(A \cap B)$, we obtain

$P(A \cap B) = P(A) + P(B) - P(A \cup B)$

$= 0.2 + 0.4 - 0.52$

$= 0.08$

> This is the generalised addition law obtained from the formula booklet.

If the events *A* and *B* are independent, then probability of both events occurring

$= P(A) \times P(B) = 0.2 \times 0.4 = 0.08$

As $P(A) \times P(B) = P(A \cap B)$, events *A* and *B* are independent.

(b) $P(A \text{ only}) = P(A) - P(A \cap B)$

$= 0.2 - 0.08$

$= 0.12$

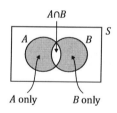

$P(B \text{ only}) = P(B) - P(A \cap B)$

$= 0.4 - 0.08$

$= 0.32$

$P(A \text{ or } B \text{ only}) = P(A \text{ only}) + P(B \text{ only}) = 0.12 + 0.32 = 0.44$

(c) Required probability $= \dfrac{P(A \text{ only occurs})}{P(A \text{ or } B \text{ only occurs})} = \dfrac{0.12}{0.44} = 0.273$ (correct to 3 d.p.)

Summary: Probability

Venn diagrams

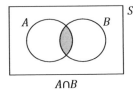

$A \cap B$

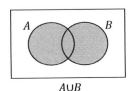

$A \cup B$

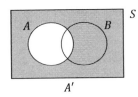

A'

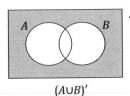

$(A \cup B)'$

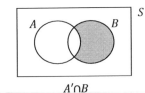

$A' \cap B$

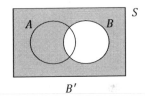

B'

Complementary events

The probability that A does not occur (i.e. A') is one minus the probability that event A does occur.

$$P(A') = 1 - P(A)$$

The meaning of independent events and mutually exclusive events

When an event has no effect on another event, they are said to be independent events. For example, if event A occurs then it will have no effect on event B happening and vice versa.

If events A and B are mutually exclusive then A or B can occur but not both.

The addition law for mutually exclusive events

$$P(A \cup B) = P(A) + P(B)$$

The generalised addition law

$$P(A \cup B) = P(A) + P(B) - P(A \cap B)$$

Multiplication law for independent events

$$P(A \cap B) = P(A) \times P(B)$$

Multiplication law for dependent events

The conditional probability of B given A is written as $P(B|A)$.

$$P(A \cap B) = P(A)P(B|A) = P(B)P(A|B)$$

The law of total probability

If $A_1, A_2, A_3, \dots, A_n$ are mutually exclusive and exhaustive events and if B is another event, we have

$$P(B) = P(A_1)\,P(B|A_1) + P(A_2)P(B|A_2) + \dots + P(A_n)P(B|A_n)$$

Bayes' theorem

If $A_1, A_2, A_3, \dots, A_n$ are mutually exclusive and exhaustive events that form the same space S and B is any event such that $P(B) > 0$, then Bayes' theorem states:

$$P(A_j|B) = \frac{P(A_j)P(B|A_j)}{\Sigma P(A_i)P(B|A_i)}$$

Permutations

A permutation is an arrangement of things. The order of things is considered in a permutation.

The number of arrangements when r objects are chosen from n is given by

$$^nP_r = \frac{n!}{(n-r)!}$$

Combinations

A combination is a selection of things. The order has no importance in a combination. The number of selections when r objects are chosen from n is given by

$$^nC_r = \frac{n!}{(n-r)!r!}$$

Topic 2 — Discrete probability distributions

This topic covers the following:

- Discrete probability distributions
- Mean/expectation
- Expected value of a function of a discrete random variable
- Standard deviation and variance
- Use of the results $E(aX + b) = aE(X) + b$ and $Var(aX + b) = a^2Var(X)$

Discrete probability distributions

The score on a die is an example of a random variable because there is no way of predicting what the score will be. As well as being a random variable, the score is also a discrete variable as only certain values (i.e. scores 1, 2, 3, 4, 5, 6) are possible. This topic deals with discrete probability distributions where there is a set of isolated values each having a certain probability of occurring.

Here is a probability distribution of a random variable X. The x values show particular values of X and the probability of each occurring is denoted by $P(X = x)$. For example $P(X = 1)$ is the probability that x takes the value 1. All the possible values x can take are shown in the table.

x	1	2	3	4
$P(X = x)$	0.2	0.4	0.3	0.1

The sum of the probabilities for the distribution shown in the table is 1, as all the values x can take are shown.

Hence $P(X = 1) + P(X = 2) + P(X = 3) + P(X = 4) = 0.2 + 0.4 + 0.3 + 0.1 = 1$

To save time the above can be written in the following way:

$$P(1) + P(2) + P(3) + P(4) = 1$$

Examples

1 The probability distribution of the discrete random variable X is given in the following table.

x	1	2	3
$P(X = x)$	0.45	0.35	a

$0.45 + 0.35 + a = 1$

Hence, $a = 0.2$

> The table shows the values of x that are possible in the sample space. The associated probabilities will add up to 1.

2 The probability distribution of the discrete random variable X is given in the following table.

x	1	2	3
$P(X = x)$	$0.6 - 2\alpha$	3α	$0.4 - \alpha$

State the range of the possible values of α

Answer

② $P(1) = 0.6 - 2\alpha$, and as a probability cannot be negative the maximum value α could have is 0.3.

Now $P(2) = 3\alpha$ and as a probability cannot be negative, the smallest value $P(2)$ can have is 0. Hence the minimum value α can have is 0. Thus $0 \le \alpha \le 0.3$.

> Note that you also need to check that $0.4 - \alpha$ does not give a smaller value. If $0.4 - \alpha = 0$ this gives $\alpha = 0.4$. So 0.4 is not the smallest value.

Mean/Expectation

The mean value of X is given the symbol μ and is also known as the expectation of X or the expected value E(X). The mean is one of the measures of average value along with the median and the mode.

For a discrete random variable X taking values x_i with probabilities p_i.

Expectation (mean): $E(X) = \mu = \Sigma x_i p_i$

> Note that this formula is included in the formula booklet so need not be remembered.

How this formula works is best seen by working through the following example.

Important note: The expectation/expected value is equal to the mean (i.e. $E(X) = \mu$)

Example

❶ The probability distribution of the discrete random variable X is given in the following table.

x	1	2	3	4
$P(X = x)$	0.15	0.3	0.35	0.2

Find E(X)

Answer

① $E(X) = \Sigma x_i p_i = 1 \times 0.15 + 2 \times 0.3 + 3 \times 0.35 + 4 \times 0.2 = 2.6$

> Notice how each value of x is multiplied by its probability and then the sum of the resulting values is found.

The expected value of a function

Let $g(X)$ be a function of the random variable X.

The expected value or expectation of $g(X)$ is denoted by E($g(X)$).

Given that X is a discrete random variable, taking values x_i with probability p_i,

$$E(g(X)) = \Sigma g(x_i)p_i$$

> This formula is included in the formula booklet and need not be remembered.

Using the above formula, the individual values of x are put into the function and multiplied by their respective probabilities. It is important to note that the probabilities for the function are the same as those for x. The sum of the values is found to determine the expected value of the function. The example in the next section explains this technique.

The expected value for E(X²)

Finding the expected value for X^2 is important as it is used in formulae to work out the variance and standard deviation.

$$E(X^2) = \Sigma x_i^2 p_i$$

Note that this is a modification of the formula $E(g(X)) = \Sigma g(x_i)p_i$ with $g(X) = X^2$ and $g(x_i)$ replaced by x_i^2 to give $E(X^2) = \Sigma x_i^2 p_i$

Important note

You cannot work out $E(X^2)$ by squaring $E(X)$, so $E(X^2) \neq (E(X))^2$

Example

❶ The probability distribution of the discrete random variable X is given in the following table.

x	1	2	3	4
$P(X=x)$	0.15	0.3	0.35	0.2

(a) Write down the probability distribution for X^2.

(b) Find $E(X^2)$

Answer

① (a)

x	1	2	3	4
x^2	1	4	9	16
$P(X=x^2)$	0.15	0.3	0.35	0.2

Notice that each value of x is squared but the probability stays the same.

(a) $E(X^2) = \Sigma x_i^2 p_i$

$= 1 \times 0.15 + 4 \times 0.3 + 9 \times 0.35 + 16 \times 0.2$

$= 7.7$

Standard deviation and variance

Standard deviation and variance are measures of dispersion (i.e. the spread of the distribution) and they are very important measures in statistics.

The standard deviation of a random variable X is given by the symbol σ, and the variance of X is written as Var(X). Var(X) and σ are related by the following formula:

$$\sigma^2 = \text{Var}(X) = E(X^2) - \mu^2.$$

In the formula booklet $E(X^2)$ is written as $\Sigma x_i^2 p_i$ to give the following formula:

$$\text{Var}(X) = \sigma^2 = \Sigma(x_i - \mu)^2 p_i = \Sigma x_i^2 p_i - \mu^2$$

This formula is included in the formula booklet and need not be remembered.

Remember that μ is the mean and has the same value as $E(X)$. This means that the above equation can be written in the following way:

$$\sigma^2 = \text{Var}(X) = E(X^2) - (E(X))^2$$

Examples

❶ A discrete random variable X has the probability distribution shown in the following table.

x	1	2	3	4
$P(X = x)$	$2a$	0.1	$0.5 - a$	$1 - 7a$

(a) Determine the value of a.

(b) Complete the following table with numerical values using your answers to part (a).

x	1	2	3	4
$P(X = x)$				

(a) Calculate:

  (i) $Var(X)$

  (ii) The standard deviation of X.

Answer

① (a) $2a + 0.1 + 0.5 - a + 1 - 7a = 1$

$$-6a + 1.6 = 1$$
$$0.6 = 6a$$

Solving, we obtain $a = 0.1$

> The probabilities for each value x can take are added together and equated to 1.

(b)

x	1	2	3	4
$P(X = x)$	0.2	0.1	0.4	0.3

> The value of a (i.e. 0.1) is substituted into the table given in the question.

(c) (i) $Var(X) = E(X^2) - \mu^2$

$E(X) = \Sigma x_i p_i = 1 \times 0.2 + 2 \times 0.1 + 3 \times 0.4$
$\qquad\qquad + 4 \times 0.3 = 2.8$

$E(X^2) = 1^2 \times 0.2 + 2^2 \times 0.1 + 3^2 \times 0.4 + 4^2 \times 0.3$

$\qquad = 1 \times 0.2 + 4 \times 0.1 + 9 \times 0.4 + 16 \times 0.3$

$\qquad = 9$

$Var(X) = E(X^2) - \mu^2 = 9 - (2.8)^2 = 1.16$

> This formula for $Var(X)$ is obtained from the formula booklet. Use the formula to see what quantities you need to find (i.e. $E(X)$ which is equal to the mean μ and $E(X^2)$).

> The formula $E(X^2) = \Sigma x_i^2 p_i$ is used here.

(ii) $\sigma^2 = Var(X)$

Hence, standard deviation, $\sigma = \sqrt{Var(X)} = \sqrt{1.16} = 1.077$
(correct to 3 d.p.)

> Remember that $E(X) = \mu$ (i.e. the expectation is equal to the mean).

❷ The probability distribution of the discrete random variable X is given by

$P(X = x) = kx^2 \quad$ for $x = 1, 2, 3, 4,$

$P(X = x) = 0 \quad$ otherwise,

where k is a constant.

(a) Show that $k = \dfrac{1}{30}$. [2]

(b) Calculate the mean and variance of X. [5]

(c) Two independent observations X_1, X_2 are taken from the distribution of X. Calculate $P(X_1 + X_2 = 4)$. [4]

(WJEC S1 June 2011 Q5)

Answer

② (a) $P(X = 1) + P(X = 2) + P(X = 3) + P(X = 4)$

$= k + 4k + 9k + 16k$

$= 30k$

Now $P(X = 1) + P(X = 2) + P(X = 3) + P(X = 4) = 1$,

so $30k = 1$, giving $k = \dfrac{1}{30}$.

> Each value x can take is substituted into the equation $P(X = x) = kx^2$.

(b) $E(X) = \dfrac{1}{30}\left(1 \times 1 + 2 \times 4 + 3 \times 9 + 4 \times 16\right) = \dfrac{10}{3}$

$E(X^2) = \dfrac{1}{30}\left(1 \times 1 + 4 \times 4 + 9 \times 9 + 16 \times 16\right) = \dfrac{59}{5}$

$Var(X) = E(X^2) - \mu^2$

$= \dfrac{59}{5} - \left(\dfrac{10}{3}\right)^2$

$= \dfrac{31}{45} = 0.689$ (correct to 3 d.p.)

> The formula $E(X) = \Sigma x_i p_i$ is used here. Notice that it is easier if the value of k is taken out as a factor.

> The formula $E(X^2) = \Sigma x_i^2 p_i$ is used here.

> Note that $E(X) = \mu$.

(c)

X_1	X_2	Probability
1	3	$\dfrac{1}{30}(1)^2 \times \dfrac{1}{30}(3)^2 = \dfrac{1}{100}$
3	1	$\dfrac{1}{30}(3)^2 \times \dfrac{1}{30}(1)^2 = \dfrac{1}{100}$
2	2	$\dfrac{1}{30}(2)^2 \times \dfrac{1}{30}(2)^2 = \dfrac{16}{900} = \dfrac{4}{225}$

> The possible values for X_1 and X_2 that give a sum of 4 are listed and then their probabilities are calculated. The required answer is the sum of these probabilities.

Required probability $= \dfrac{1}{100} + \dfrac{1}{100} + \dfrac{4}{225} = \dfrac{17}{450} = 0.0378$ (correct to 4 d.p.)

❸ The probability distribution of the discrete random variable X is given in the following table, where λ is a constant.

x	2	3	4	5	6
$P(X = x)$	0.1	0.2	0.3	λ	$0.4 - \lambda$

(a) Find the range of possible values of λ. [2]

(b) Given that $E(X) = 4 \cdot 25$,

    (i) find the value of λ

    (ii) evaluate $Var(X)$. [6]

(WJEC S1 Jan 2010 Q4)

Answer

③ (a) $P(6) = 0.4 - \lambda$ and as probability cannot be negative the maximum value λ could have is 0.4.

Now $P(5) = \lambda$ and as probability cannot be negative, the smallest value $P(5)$ can have is 0.

Hence, range of possible values of λ is [0, 0.4]

> Note that $P(2) + P(3) + P(4) + P(5) + P(6) = 1$, whatever the value of λ.

> Note that range is given in square brackets with the smallest and then largest value separated by a comma.

(b) (i) $E(X) = \mu = \Sigma x_i p_i$

$E(X) = 2 \times 0.1 + 3 \times 0.2 + 4 \times 0.3 + 5\lambda + 6(0.4 - \lambda) = 4.4 - \lambda$

Now $E(X) = 4.25$ so $4.4 - \lambda = 4.25$

Hence, $\lambda = 0.15$

> This formula for E(X) is obtained from the formula booklet.

(ii) $E(X)^2 = 4 \times 0.1 + 9 \times 0.2 + 16 \times 0.3 + 25 \times 0.15 + 36 \times 0.25$

$= 19.75$

$Var(X) = E(X^2) - \mu^2$

$= 19.75 - 4.25^2$

$= 1.6875$

> Note that each value of x is squared and multiplied by its probability.

> This formula for Var(X) is obtained from the formula booklet.

Use of the results E(aX + b) = aE(X) + b and Var(aX + b) = a²Var(X)

There are two important formulae for the expected value and variance of a linear function of X and they are:

$$E(aX + b) = aE(X) + b$$
$$Var(aX + b) = a^2Var(X)$$

> **Neither** of these formulae are included in the formula booklet and will need to be remembered.

For example, if you had the following function of X:

$Y = 4X - 1$, then $E(Y) = E(4X - 1) = 4E(X) - 1$ and $Var(Y) = Var(4x - 1) = 4^2Var(X) = 16Var(X)$.

If $E(X)$ and $Var(X)$ are known then these can be substituted into the equations and numerical values for the expected value and variance of $aX + b$ can be found. The following examples illustrate this technique.

Examples

❶ The random variable X has mean 6 and variance 3. The random variable Y is given by

$Y = 3X + 2$.

Find the mean and variance of Y.

Answer

① Using $E(aX + b) = aE(X) + b$, we obtain

$E(3X + 2) = 3E(X) + 2$.

Now, $E(X) = 6$, so $E(3X + 2) = 3 \times 6 + 2 = 20$

Hence, $E(Y) = 20$

Now $Var(aX + b) = a^2Var(X)$

Now, $Var(X) = 3$, so $Var(3X + 2) = 3^2(Var\ X)$

$= 9 \times 3$

$= 27$

Hence, $Var(Y) = 27$

❷ The random variable X has mean 4 and variance 2. The random variable Y is given by $Y = 3X - 1$.

(a) Find the mean and variance of Y. [4]

(b) Hence find the value of $E(Y^2)$. [2]

(WJEC S1 June 2010 Q2)

Answer

② (a) $E(aX + b) = aE(X) + b$

| This formula will need to be recalled as it is not in the formula booklet. |

$E(Y) = E(3X - 1) = 3E(X) - 1 = 3 \times 4 - 1 = 11$

$Var(aX + b) = a^2Var(X)$

| This formula will need to be recalled as it is not in the formula booklet. |

$Var(Y) = Var(3X - 1) = 3^2Var(X) = 9 \times 2 = 18$

(b) $E(Y^2) = Var(Y) + \{E(Y)\}^2$

$= 18 + 121$

$= 139$

❸ The probability distribution of the discrete variable X is given in the following table.

x	1	2	3	4
$P(X = x)$	0.15	p	0.20	q

(a) Show that $p + q = 0.65$.

(b) Given that $E(X) = 2.35$, show that $p = 0.5$ and $q = 0.15$.

(c) Find the variance of X.

(d) The random variable Y is defined by $Y = 3X - 1$.

(i) Find the mean and variance of Y.

(ii) Find $P(Y < 7)$.

Answer

③ (a) $P(1) + P(2) + P(3) + P(4) = 1$

Hence, $0.15 + p + 0.20 + q = 1$

$p + q = 0.65$ (1)

(b) $E(X) = \mu = \Sigma x_i p_i$

| This formula is looked up in the formula booklet. |

Hence, $2.35 = 1 \times 0.15 + 2p + 3 \times 0.20 + 4q$

$2.35 = 0.75 + 2p + 4q$

$2p + 4q = 1.6$ (2)

Multiplying equation (1) by 2, we obtain

$2p + 2q = 1.30$

Subtraction of the above equation from equation (2) gives

$2q = 0.3$

$q = 0.15$

Substituting this value of q into equation (1) we obtain

$p + 0.15 = 0.65$

Hence, $p = 0.5$

(c) $\text{Var}(X) = E(X^2) - \mu^2$

Now $E(X^2) = \Sigma x_i^2 p_i = 1^2 \times 0.15 + 2^2 \times 0.5 + 3^2 \times 0.2 + 4^2 \times 0.15 = 6.35$

Hence, $\text{Var}(X) = E(X^2) - \mu^2 = 6.35 - 2.35^2 = 0.8275$

(d) (i) Using $E(aX + b) = aE(X) + b$, we obtain

$\quad E(Y) = E(3X - 1) = 3E(X) - 1.$

$\qquad = 3 \times 2.35 - 1$

$\qquad = 6.05$

Using $\text{Var}(aX + b) = a^2\text{Var}(X)$, we obtain

$\text{Var}(Y) = \text{Var}(3X - 1) = 3^2\text{Var}(X) = 9 \times 0.8275 = 7.4475$

(ii) $Y = 3X - 1$

As $Y < 7$, $3X - 1 < 7$, so $x < 2.667$ and as this is a discrete probability distribution, the values x can take are 1 and 2.

Hence, $P(Y < 7) = P(1) + P(2) = 0.15 + 0.5 = 0.65$

Examination style questions

1 The probability distribution of the discrete random variable X is given by

$\quad P(X = x) = k\,(1+2x) \qquad$ for $x = 1, 2, 3, 4,$

$\quad P(X = x) = 0 \qquad\qquad$ otherwise,

where k is a constant.

(a) Show that $k = \frac{1}{24}$. [2]

(b) Calculate the mean and variance of X. [5]

Answer

① (a)

x	1	2	3	4
$P(X = x)$	$3k$	$5k$	$7k$	$9k$

Now $3k + 5k + 7k + 9k = 1$,

so $24k = 1$, giving $k = \frac{1}{24}$.

(b) $E(X) = \mu = \Sigma x_i p_i$

$\mu = \frac{1}{24}\left(1 \times 3 + 2 \times 5 + 3 \times 7 + 4 \times 9\right) = 2.917$ (correct to 3 d.p.)

$E(X)^2 = \Sigma x_i^2 p_i$

$\qquad = \frac{1}{24}(1^2 \times 3 + 2^2 \times 5 + 3^2 \times 7 + 4^2 \times 9)$

$\qquad = \frac{1}{24}(1 \times 3 + 4 \times 5 + 9 \times 7 + 16 \times 9)$

$\qquad = 9.583$ (correct to 3 d.p.)

$\text{Var}(X) = E(X^2) - \mu^2$

$\qquad = 9.583 - (2.917)^2$

$\qquad = 1.07$ (correct to 2 d.p.)

> Note that it is easier in this calculation to take the $\frac{1}{24}$ out as a factor.

> This formula for $\text{Var}(X)$ is obtained from the formula booklet.

❷ The probability distribution of the discrete random variable X is given by

$$P(X = x) = \frac{x}{16} \qquad \text{for } x = 1, 3, 5, 7,$$
$$P(X = x) = 0 \qquad \text{otherwise.}$$

Given that X_1 and X_2 are two independent values of X, determine

(a) $P(X_1 + X_2 = 10)$ [3]

(b) $P(X_1 = X_2)$ [3]

Answer

② (a) To make 10 there are the following possibilities for X_1 and X_2.

(3, 7), (7, 3), (5, 5)

$$P(X_1 + X_2 = 10) = \left(\frac{3}{16} \times \frac{7}{16}\right) + \left(\frac{7}{16} \times \frac{3}{16}\right) + \left(\frac{5}{16} \times \frac{5}{16}\right) = \frac{67}{256} = 0.2617 \text{ (correct to 4 d.p.)}$$

(b) For X_1 and X_2 to be equal there are the following possibilities

(1, 1), (3, 3), (5, 5), (7, 7)

$$P(X_1 = X_2) = \left(\frac{1}{16}\right)^2 + \left(\frac{3}{16}\right)^2 + \left(\frac{5}{16}\right)^2 + \left(\frac{7}{16}\right)^2 = \frac{21}{64} = 0.3281 \text{ (correct to 4 d.p.)}$$

Note the probability of obtaining (1, 1) is $\frac{1}{16} \times \frac{1}{16} = \left(\frac{1}{16}\right)^2$. All the probabilities of all the other possible pairs are worked out in a similar way and then added together to give the required probability.

Test yourself

Answer the following questions and check your answers before moving onto the next topic.

1 The probability distribution of the discrete random variable X is given by

$P(X = x) = k(5 - x)$ for $x = 1, 2, 3, 4,$

$P(X = x) = 0$ otherwise,

where k is a constant.

(a) Show that $k = \frac{1}{10}$.

(b) Calculate $E(X)$ and $\text{Var}(X)$

2 The random variable X has mean 4 and variance 2. The random variable Y is given by

$Y = 2X + 1.$

(a) Find the mean and variance of Y.

(b) Hence find the value of $E(Y^2)$.

3 The discrete random variable X has the following probability distribution

x	1	2	3
$P(X = x)$	0.2	0.4	0.4

Given that $E(X) = 2.2,$

(a) Calculate the standard deviation of X.

(b) Calculate $E(1/X)$

4 The probability distribution of the discrete random variable X is given by

$P(X = x) = kx$ for $x = 2, 4, 6,$

$P(X = x) = 0$ otherwise,

where k is a constant.

(a) Calculate the value of k.

(b) Determine

(i) $E(X),$

(ii) $E\left(\frac{1}{X}\right).$

1   The probability distribution of the discrete random variable X is given by

$P(X = x) = kx$ for $x = 1, 3, 5, 7$,

$P(X = x) = 0$ otherwise.

(a)   Show that $k = \frac{1}{16}$.   [2]

(b)   Determine

    (i) $E(X)$,

    (ii) $E\left(\frac{1}{X}\right)$.   [5]

(c)   Given that X_1, X_2 are two independent values of X, determine

    (i) $P(X_1 + X_2 = 6)$,

    (ii) $P(X_1 = X_2)$.   [7]

(WJEC S1 June 2010 Q6)

Answer

1   (a) $P(X = 1) + P(X = 3) + P(X = 5) + P(X = 7) = k + 3k + 5k + 7k = 16k$

Now $P(X = 1) + P(X = 3) + P(X = 5) + P(X = 7) = 1$,

so $16k = 1$, giving $k = \frac{1}{16}$.

(b)   (i) $E(X) = \mu = \Sigma x_i p_i$

$= \frac{1}{16}\left(1 \times 1 + 3 \times 3 + 5 \times 5 + 7 \times 7\right) = 5.25$

    (ii) $E\left(\frac{1}{X}\right) = \left(\frac{1}{16}\right)\left(\frac{1}{1} \times 1 + \frac{1}{3} \times 3 + \frac{1}{5} \times 5 + \frac{1}{7} \times 7\right) = 0.25$

(c)   (i)   To obtain 6 there are the following possibilities for X_1 and X_2 :

$(1, 5), (5, 1)$ and $(3, 3)$.

Hence $P(X_1 + X_2 = 6) = \frac{1}{16} \times \frac{5}{16} + \frac{5}{16} \times \frac{1}{16} + \frac{3}{16} \times \frac{3}{16} = \frac{19}{256}$ or 0.074 (3 d.p.)

    (ii)   To obtain $X_1 = X_2$ there are the following possibilities:

$(1, 1), (3, 3), (5, 5), (7, 7)$

Hence $P(X_1 = X_2) = \frac{1}{16} \times \frac{1}{16} + \frac{3}{16} \times \frac{3}{16} + \frac{5}{16} \times \frac{5}{16} + \frac{7}{16} \times \frac{7}{16} = \frac{21}{64}$ or 0.328 (3 d.p.)

Q&A

2

2   The random variable X is such that $E(X) = 5$ and $Var(X) = 4$. The random variable Y is defined by $Y = aX - b$ where a, b are positive constants. Given that $E(Y) = 0$ and $Var(Y) = 1$, find the values of a and b.

[6]

(WJEC S1 June 2007 Q3)

Answer

2    $E(aX + b) = aE(X) + b$

Hence as $Y = aX - b$, $E(Y) = E(aX - b) = aE(X) - b$

and as $E(X) = 5$ and $E(Y) = 0$, we have

$$0 = 5a - b \qquad\qquad (1)$$

Also $Var(aX + b) = a^2Var(X)$

Hence as $Y = aX - b$, $Var(Y) = Var(aX - b) = a^2Var(X)$

and as $Var(X) = 4$ and $Var(Y) = 1$ we have,

$$1 = 4a^2$$

Hence, $a^2 = \frac{1}{4}$ so $a = \pm\frac{1}{2}$

As, a is a positive constant $a = \frac{1}{2}$

Substituting $a = \frac{1}{2}$ into equation (1) gives

$$0 = 5\left(\frac{1}{2}\right) - b$$

Hence, $b = \frac{5}{2}$

 Grade boost

If there are two answers, always check with the question to see if one of the answers can be rejected.

Summary: Discrete probability distribution

A discrete probability distribution for a random variable X, is a set of isolated values each having a certain probability of occurring. The distribution can be shown in a table like this:

x	5	6	7	8
$P(X = x)$	0.15	0.35	0.45	0.05

The probabilities in the table, add up to 1. The mean, variance and standard deviation can be calculated from the values in this table using the formulae in the section below.

Mean, variance, and standard deviation

For a discrete random variable X taking values x_i with probabilities p_i

Expectation (mean): $E(X) = \mu = \sum x_i\, p_i$

Variance: $Var(X) = \sigma^2 = \sum(x_i - \mu)^2 p_i = \sum x_i^2 p_i - \mu^2$ where σ = standard deviation,

$$\mu = \text{mean}$$

The expectation of a function

The expected value or expectation of a function of X called $E(g(X))$, where X is a discrete random variable taking values x_i with probabilities p_i, is given by

$$E(g(X)) = \sum g(x_i) p_i$$

The expected value for $E(X^2)$

$$E(X^2) = \sum x_i^2 p_i$$

Expectation and variance of a linear function

There are two important results:

$$E(aX + b) = aE(X) + b$$
$$Var(aX + b) = a^2 Var(X)$$

Topic 3 — Binomial and Poisson distributions

This topic covers the following:

- Bernoulli trials and the binomial distribution
- The Poisson distribution
- Mean and variance of binomial and Poisson distributions
- Poisson approximation to a binomial

Bernoulli trials

A Bernoulli trial is an experiment whose outcome is random and can be either of two possible outcomes 'success' or 'failure'.

In order to conduct a Bernoulli trial the question needs to be phrased in such a way that the event can be categorised into success if it takes place or failure if it doesn't.

For example, you could ask the question 'did the die land on a 6?' If it did then this would be considered success and if it didn't, it would be classed as failure. Independent repeated trials of an experiment with two outcomes only are called Bernoulli trials.

If p is the probability of success in a Bernoulli trial and q is the probability of failure, then we have the result:

$$p + q = 1$$

> The probability of success p added to the probability of failure q will add up to one.

Binomial distribution

A binomial experiment is closely related to a Bernoulli experiment. It consists of a fixed number of trials, n, each with a probability p of occurring and it counts the number of successes, x. This is sometimes abbreviated in the following way $B(n, p)$. The binomial distribution is a discrete probability distribution and the probability of a particular number of successes, x, occurring is given by the following formula:

$$P(X = x) = \binom{n}{x} p^x (1 - p)^{n - x}$$

> Note that this formula is included in the formula booklet.

Note that $\binom{n}{x}$ can also be written as ^nC_x so when there are numerical values for n and x, these can be substituted into your calculator for n and x to obtain a value for $\binom{n}{x}$. It is important to note that on many calculators the x is replaced by an r to give ^nC_r. $1 - p = q$ which is the probabilty of failure.

The binomial distribution formula can only be used with:

- Independent trials (i.e. where the probability of one event does not depend on another).
- Trials where there is a constant probability of success.
- A fixed number of trials.
- Where there is only success or failure.

Use your calculator to work out the following and check you obtain the answers shown.

⚜ Grade boost

You are often asked about the conditions for using the binomial distribution in exam questions. You need to remember these conditions.

Examples

❶ Work out the following:

(a) $\binom{5}{0}$ (b) $\binom{5}{1}$ (c) $\binom{8}{5}$ (d) $\binom{10}{5}$

Answer

① (a) $\binom{5}{0} = 1$ (b) $\binom{5}{1} = 5$ (c) $\binom{8}{5} = 56$ (d) $\binom{10}{5} = 252$

❷ A salesperson makes 60 calls to potential customers during a particular week. The probability of making a sale at each call is independent of other calls and is 0.3.

Find the probability that during a particular week, he makes:

(a) Exactly 10 sales.

(b) Exactly 19 or 20 sales.

Answer

② (a) Using $(X = x) = \binom{n}{x}p^x(1 - p)^{n-x}$,

with $x = 10$, $n = 60$ and $p = 0.3$ we obtain

$P(X = 10) = \binom{60}{10} 0.3^{10}(1 - 0.3)^{60-10}$

$= \binom{60}{10} 0.3^{10}(0.7)^{50}$

$= 0.008$ (correct to 3 decimal places)

> Note the assumptions in using the binomial distribution.

(b) Using $P(X = x) = \binom{n}{x}p^x(1 - p)^{n-x}$,

with $x = 19$, $n = 60$ and $p = 0.3$ we obtain

$P(X = 19) = \binom{60}{19} 0.3^{19}(1 - 0.3)^{60-19}$

$= \binom{60}{19} 0.3^{19}(0.7)^{41}$

$= 0.1059$ (correct to 4 decimal places)

> Use the formula for the binomial distribution $P(X = x) = \binom{n}{x}p^x(1 - p)^{n-x}$ which is obtained from the formula booklet.

Using $(X = x) = \binom{n}{x}p^x(1 - p)^{n-x}$,

with $x = 20$, $n = 60$ and $p = 0.3$ we obtain

$P(X = 20) = \binom{60}{20} 0.3^{20}(1 - 0.3)^{60-20}$

$= \binom{60}{20} 0.3^{20}(0.7)^{40}$

$= 0.0931$ (correct to 4 decimal places)

Now, $P(X = 19$ or $20) = P(X = 19) + P(X = 20)$

$= 0.1059 + 0.0931$

$= 0.199$ (correct to 3 decimal places)

> The probability of obtaining 19 or 20 is found by adding the two probabilities together.

The mean and variance of binomial distributions

There are formulae for the mean and variance of a binomial distribution.

If X has the distribution B (n, p) then,

$$\text{Mean} = np$$

Variance, $\qquad \text{Var}(X) = np(1 - p)$

> Both of these formulae are obtained from the formula booklet.

The standard deviation, σ, is related to the variance by the following equation:

$$\sigma^2 = \text{Var}(X) \text{ so } \sigma = \sqrt{\text{Var}(X)}$$

Examples

❶ The random variable X has the binomial distribution B$(n, 0.2)$. Given that the mean of X is twice its standard deviation, find the value of n.

[5]

(WJEC S1 Jan 2011 Q4)

Answer

① $p = 0.2$ and as Mean $= np$, Mean $= 0.2n$

$\text{Var}(X) = np(1 - p) = 0.2n(1 - 0.2) = 0.16n$

Now $\sigma^2 = \text{Var}(X)$ so $\sigma = \sqrt{\text{Var}(X)} = \sqrt{0.16n}$

Now Mean $= 2\sigma$,

so $0.2n = 2\sqrt{0.16n}$

Squaring both sides, we obtain $0.04n^2 = 4 \times 0.16n$

Hence $0.04n^2 - 0.64n = 0$

And $n^2 - 16n = 0$ so $n(n - 16) = 0$

Hence, $n = 16$.

> Note there are two solutions, $n = 0$ and $n = 16$. $n = 0$ is ignored because n is the number of trials which cannot be zero. Hence $n = 16$.

❷ The random variable X has the binomial distribution B(n, p). If the mean and standard deviation of X are 10 and 3 respectively, find the values of n and p.

Answer

② Mean $= np = 10$

Now $\text{Var}(X) = \sigma^2 = 3^2 = 9$

$\text{Var}(X) = np(1 - p)$

Hence $9 = np(1 - p)$ $\qquad\qquad\qquad$ (1)

Substituting $np = 10$ into equation (1) we obtain

$\qquad 9 = 10(1 - p)$

$\qquad 9 = 10 - 10p$

Solving, gives $p = \frac{1}{10} = 0.1$

Now as $np = 10$ and as $p = 0.1$ we have

$0.1n = 10$, giving $n = 100$.

Using binomial distribution tables to determine probabilities

Finding probabilities using the formula is tedious in some situations but luckily there is a quicker way of finding them than by calculation. Tables of the binomial distribution function can be used. These tables are provided in the exam and you must familiarise yourself with using them.

In this course, two alternative types of table are used, namely *Elementary Statistical Tables* (RND tables) and *Statistical Tables* by Murdoch and Barnes (MB tables). You should use only one of these sets of tables.

The essential differences of the tables are as follows:

RND	Murdoch and Barnes (MB)
The table gives $$P(X \leq x) = \sum_{r=0}^{x} \binom{n}{r} p^r (1-p)^{n-r}$$ i.e. Probability of less than or equal to x successes	The table gives $$P(X \geq r) = \sum_{x=r}^{n} \binom{n}{x} p^x (1-p)^{n-x}$$ i.e. Probability of greater than or equal to r successes

To use the tables you firstly need to check carefully that you are using the correct table in the booklet of statistical tables.

There are three quantities that you need in order to obtain the probability in the table, which are:

> n, the total number of trials
>
> x, the number of successes (for RND tables) or r, the number of successes (for MB tables)
>
> p, the probability of success

For example, suppose that the probability of a particular component being rejected in a batch is 0.3 independently of all other components. Suppose we have $n = 10$, $p = 0.3$ and x or $r = 3$.

Let us explore the outputs of the tables for these values.

Note that if the above quantities are used in the table we will be finding $P(X \leq 3)$ for RND or $P(X \geq 3)$ for Murdoch and Barnes (MB).

> Note that in the question, 3 or fewer would include 3. Hence we are finding the probability of 0, 1, 2 or 3 components being rejected.

The tables are used in the following way.

- First you have to find the correct table in the booklet. Here you are using the binomial distribution function tables.
- Look for the section which refers to the value of n (i.e. 10 in this case).
- You then look down the column and select the value for x or r (i.e. 3 in this case).
- Then look at the probability headings at the top of the page to find the required value for p (0.30 in this case). Read off the intersection between the value for x or r and the value for p and you have the probability. Check that for this example you obtain the probability of 0.6496 (RND) or 0.6172 (MB).

It is important to note than RND gives a probability of *less* than or equal to a number of successes whilst MB gives a probability of *greater* than or equal to a number of successes.

So if you wanted to find the probability of 4 successes for $n = 10$, $p = 0.3$, you would proceed as follows.

RND	Murdoch and Barnes (MB)
$P(X = 4) = P(X \leq 4) - P(X \leq 3)$ $= 0.8497 - 0.6496$ $= 0.2001$ i.e. find the probability (4 or less) – probability (3 or less)	$P(X = 4) = P(X \geq 4) - P(X \geq 5)$ $= 0.3504 - 0.1503$ $= 0.2001$ i.e. find the probability (4 or more) – probability (5 or more)

You could still use the formula to find the probability and this would be a valid method if no indication of which method to use were given in the question.

Note

Whilst the examples in the book use mainly RND tables, an alternative presentation of the remainder of this topic is given in an appendix on page 90. It is only necessary to refer to this appendix if your school or college uses MB tables.

Examples

❶ When cuttings of a certain plant are taken, the probability of each cutting rooting is 0.25 independently of all other cuttings.

Joshua takes 20 cuttings. Find the probability that at least 10 of the cuttings take root.

Answer

① Here we have $n = 20$, $p = 0.25$ and $x = 10$.

Using the tables we obtain a probability for $P(X \leq 9) = 0.9861$

Required probability, $P(X \geq 10) = 1 - 0.9861 = 0.0139$

> Here we will use the binomial distribution function table to work out the total probability of 9 or less taking root. Once found, we can take the answer from one to find the required probability.

❷ The probability that a machine part fails in its first year is 0.05 independently of all other parts. In a batch of 20 randomly selected parts, find the probability that in the first year:

(a) exactly 1 part fails

(b) more than 2 parts fail.

Answer

② (a) Using $(X = x) = \binom{n}{x} p^x (1 - p)^{n-x}$,

with $x = 1$, $n = 20$ and $p = 0.05$ we obtain

$P(X = 1) = \binom{20}{1} 0.05^1 (1 - 0.05)^{20-1}$

$= \binom{20}{1} 0.05^1 (0.95)^{19}$

$= 0.3773536$

$= 0.3774$ (correct to 4 s.f.)

> Note that no method is specified in the question so for the answer you can use the binomial formula or use the tables.

Alternative method using tables with $n = 20$ and $p = 0.05$ we have

$P(X = 1) = P(X \leq 1) - P(X \leq 0)$

$= 0.7358 - 0.3585$

$= 0.3773$

> Note the slight difference in the answers between the calculated probability and the probability found using tables. This is caused by rounding off in the tables.

(b) $P(X > 2) = 1 - P(X \leq 2) = 1 - 0.9245$

$= 0.0755$

> Tables have been used here but the binomial formula could also be used.

What to do if $P > 0.5$, as the tables do not show values above $P = 0.5$

It should be noted that in the tables for the binomial distribution the highest value of p considered is 0.50. When dealing with binomial distributions in which $p > 0.5$, we note that the probability of a failure $q = 1 - p < 0.5$. In this case, we consider the number of failures instead of the number of successes.

Examples

❶ Given that X has the binomial distribution B $(12, 0.6)$, find the values of

(a) $P(X = 8)$

(b) $P(6 \leq X \leq 10)$.

Answer

① Let $Y = 12 - X$

Then Y has the distribution B $(12, 0.4)$

> X is the number of successes.
> Y is the number of failures.

(a) $P(X = 8) = P(Y = 4) = P(Y \leq 4) - P(Y \leq 3)$

$= 0.4382 - 0.2253$

$= 0.2129$

(b) $P(6 \leq X \leq 10) = P(2 \leq Y \leq 6)$

$= P(Y \leq 6) - P(Y \leq 1)$

$= 0.8418 - 0.0196$

$= 0.8222$

❷ The probability that a randomly chosen daffodil bulb will produce a flower is 0.8. If 20 such bulbs are planted, find the probabilities that:

(a) exactly 12 of them will produce flowers

(b) fewer than 8 will produce flowers.

Answer

② Let X be the number of bulbs that produce flowers, so that X is distributed as B $(20, 0.8)$.

Since $p = 0.8 > 0.5$ we consider $Y = 20 - X$ and note that Y is distributed as B $(20, 0.2)$.

(a) $P(X = 12) = P(Y = 8)$

> X is the number of successes.
> Y is the number of failures.

$= P(Y \leq 8) - P(Y \leq 7)$

$= 0.9900 - 0.9679$

$= 0.0221$

(b) $P(X < 8) = P(X \leq 7) = P(Y \geq 13)$

$P(Y \geq 13) = 1 - P(Y \leq 12)$

$= 1 - 1$

$= 0$

The Poisson distribution

The Poisson distribution is a discrete probability distribution and is used to model the number of events occurring randomly within a given interval of time and space.

In a particular interval, the probability of an event X occurring x number of times is given by the following formula

$$P(X = x) = e^{-\lambda}\frac{\lambda^x}{x!} \text{ where } \lambda = \mu = E(X) \text{ and } x = 0, 1, 2, 3, 4, \ldots$$

> Note that this formula is given in the formula booklet.

If the probabilities of X are distributed in this way, we write

$$X \sim Po\,(\lambda)$$

Note that the symbol $\sim$ means 'is distributed'.

λ is the parameter of the distribution. We say X is distributed with a Poisson with parameter λ.

Example

❶ Use the random variable $X \sim Po\,(1.4)$ to determine:

(a) $P(X = 2)$

(b) $P(X \geq 1)$

> The formula $P(X = x) = e^{-\lambda}\frac{\lambda^x}{x!}$ is looked up in the formula booklet and used here.

(c) $P(2 < X \leq 4)$

Answer

① (a) $P(X = 2) = e^{-1.4}\dfrac{1.4^2}{2!}$

   $= 0.2417$

(b) $P(X \geq 1) = 1 - P(X = 0)$

> $P(X \geq 1)$ means the probability of x being 1, 2, 3, ... Note that it does not include the probability of x being 0. Hence we can subtract the probability of $P(X = 0)$ from 1.

   $= 1 - \left(e^{-1.4}\dfrac{1.4^0}{0!}\right)$

> Note that $1.4^0 = 1$ and also that $0! = 1$.

   $= 1 - 0.2466$

   $= 0.7534$

(c) $P(2 < X \leq 4) = P(X = 3) + P(X = 4)$

   $= e^{-1.4}\dfrac{1.4^3}{3!} + e^{-1.4}\dfrac{1.4^4}{4!}$

   $= 0.1128 + 0.0395$

   $= 0.152$ (correct to 3 decimal places)

Using tables we obtain the following results

Grade boost

Remember to read inequalities very carefully. Many students fail to do this. Here many students will incorrectly also include $P(X = 2)$.

(a) $P(X = 2) = P(X \leq 2) - P(X \leq 1) = 0.8335 - 0.5918 = 0.2417$

(b) $P(X \geq 1) = 1 - P(X = 0) = 1 - 0.2466 = 0.7534$

(c) $P(2 < X \leq 4) = P(3 \leq X \leq 4) = P(X \leq 4) - P(X \leq 2)$

   $= 0.9857 - 0.8335$

   $= 0.1522$

Mean and variance of the Poisson distribution

There are formulae for the mean and variance of a Poisson distribution.

If X is $Po\,(\lambda)$ then, Mean $\mu = \lambda$, Variance $= \lambda$.

Using the Poisson distribution to approximate the binomial distribution

Both the binomial and Poisson distributions are discrete probability distributions.

In general we can approximate the binomial distribution by using the Poisson distribution in the following circumstances:

> If n is large (usually > 50) and
>
> p is small (usually <0.1).

In the above circumstances B(n, p) can be approximated by Po(λ) where $\lambda = np$.

> ### ⚜ Grade boost
> Do not get these mixed up with the conditions needed to be able to use the binomial distribution to solve a problem.

Using Poisson distribution function tables to work out $P(X \le x)$

Poisson distribution function tables can be used to work out $P(X \le x)$. For example, if you wanted to find $P(X \le 3)$ for a distribution Po(0.8) you would look up the intersection of the row where $x = 3$ with the column where λ or $m = 0.8$ to give the required probability of 0.9909.

Example

❶ Given that 5% of pupils in a school are left-handed, use the Poisson distribution to estimate the probability that a random sample of 100 pupils in the school contains two or more left-handed pupils.

Answer

① $\lambda = np = 100 \times 0.05 = 5$

X is approximately distributed as Po(5)

$P(X \ge 2) = 1 - P(X \le 1)$

$\qquad = 1 - 0.0404$

$\qquad = 0.9596$

❷ The random variable X has the binomial distribution B (300, 0.012). Use a Poisson approximation to find an approximate value for the probability that X is less than 3.

Answer

② Mean $= np = 300 \times 0.012 = 3.6$

X is approximately distributed as Po (3.6) (i.e. $X \sim$ Po(3.6))

$P(X < 3) = P(X \le 2)$

$\qquad = 0.3027$

> Compare B(300, 0.012) with B(n, p) gives $n = 300$ and $p = 0.012$.

> Note that this means the parameter $\lambda = 3.6$.

❸ Cars arrive at a petrol station in such a way that the number arriving during an interval of length t minutes has a Poisson distribution with mean $0.2t$.

(a) Find the probability that:

(i) exactly ten cars arrive between 9 a.m. and 10 a.m.,

(ii) more than five cars arrive between 11 a.m. and 11.30 a.m. [6]

(b) The probability that no cars arrive during an interval of length t minutes is equal to 0.03. Without the use of tables, find the value of t. [4]

(WJEC S1 June 2011 Q4)

Answer

③ (a) (i) Mean $\lambda = 0.2t$ and over 60 min (i.e. 1 hr) $\lambda = 0.2 \times 60 = 12$

X is distributed as Po(12)

$$P(X = 10) = e^{-12}\frac{12^{10}}{10!} = 0.1048 \text{ (correct to 4 s.f.)}$$

$P(X = 10) = P(X \le 10) - P(X \le 9)$
$= 0.3472 - 0.2424$
$= 0.1048$

(ii) Mean $\lambda = 0.2t$ and over 30 min (i.e. 0.5 hr) $\lambda = 0.2 \times 30 = 6$

X is Po(6)

$P(X > 5) = 1 - P(X \le 5) = 1 - 0.4457 = 0.5543$ (correct to 4 s.f.)

(b) Mean $\lambda = 0.2t$

$$P(X = 0) = e^{-0.2t}\frac{(0.2t)^0}{0!}$$

$P(X = 0) = e^{-0.2t}$

Note that $P(X \le 5)$ is found by using tables.

Note that $(0.2t)^0 = 1$ and also that $0! = 1$.

Now, $P(X = 0) = 0.03$

Hence, $e^{-0.2t} = 0.03$

Taking $\log_e$ of both sides, we obtain

$-0.2t = \log_e 0.03$

Solving, gives $t = 17.5$ min (correct to one decimal place).

Note that the solving of equations by the use of logarithms was covered in Core 2. Instead of taking $\log_e$ of both sides you could have used $\log_{10}$.

Examination style questions

1 The number of parcels per day arriving at a school has a Poisson distribution with a mean of 2.5, independently of all other days.

    (a) Without the use of tables, find the probability that on a randomly selected day:

        (i) no parcels arrive

        (ii) either 4 or 5 parcels arrive.   [5]

    (b) Over a 3-day period, calculate the probability that

        (i) no parcels arrive

        (ii) the first parcel that arrives, arrives on the third day.   [5]

Answer

① (a) (i) Using $P(X = x) = e^{-\lambda}\dfrac{\lambda^x}{x!}$, we obtain

$$P(X = 0) = e^{-2.5}\frac{2.5^0}{0!}$$

$$= 0.0821$$

> The equation $P(X = x) = e^{-\lambda}\dfrac{\lambda^x}{x!}$ is used here which is obtained from the formula booklet.

    (ii) Using $P(X = 4 \text{ or } 5) = e^{-2.5}\dfrac{2.5^4}{4!} + e^{-2.5}\dfrac{2.5^5}{5!}$

$$= 0.1336 + 0.0668$$

$$= 0.200 \text{ (correct to 3 decimal places)}$$

> Note that $2.5^0 = 1$ and also that $0! = 1$.

> The probability of 4 parcels arriving is found and added to the probability of 5 parcels arriving.

    (b) (i) P(no parcels arriving over 3 days) = $0.0821 \times 0.0821 \times 0.0821$

$$= 0.0821^3$$

$$= 0.00055$$

        (ii) There must be no parcels on the first day or the second day.

        P(no parcels arriving until the third day) = $0.0821 \times 0.0821 \times (1 - 0.0821)$

$$= 0.0062$$

        (correct to 4 decimal places)

> Notice that the probabilities are multiplied together. You can only do this for independent events (i.e. where the probabilities stay constant).

❷ The random variable X has the distribution B$(n, 0.2)$ where $n \neq 0$. Given that the mean and standard deviation of X are equal, find the value of n. [5]

Answer

② $p = 0.2$ and as mean $= np = 0.2n$,

$\text{Var}(X) = np(1 - p) = 0.2n(1 - 0.2) = 0.16n$.

Now Mean $= \sigma$,

so $0.2n = \sqrt{0.16n}$ (given)

Squaring both sides, we obtain $0.04n^2 = 0.16n$

Hence $0.04n^2 - 0.16n = 0$

so $n(0.04n - 0.16) = 0$

Hence, $n = 4$.

> Note there are two solutions, $n = 0$ and $n = 4$. $n = 0$ is ignored because $n \neq 0$ in the question. Hence $n = 4$.

❸ On a turtle farm, turtles are bred and hatched from eggs under controlled conditions.

(a) The probability of producing a female turtle from an egg is 0.4 under the controlled conditions. The probability of producing a female from an egg is independent of other eggs hatching to produce female turtles. When 20 eggs are kept under the controlled conditions, find the probability that:

   (i) exactly 10 female turtles are produced

   (ii) more than 7 female turtles are produced. [5]

(b) During the hatching process, the probability that an egg fails to hatch is 0.05. When 300 eggs are kept under the controlled conditions, use the Poisson approximation to find the probability that the number of eggs failing to hatch is fewer than 10. [3]

Answer

③ (a) (i) $P(X = x) = \binom{n}{x}p^x(1 - p)^{n - x}$

   $p = 0.4, n = 20$ and $x = 10$.

   $P(X = 10) = \binom{20}{10}0.4^{10}(1 - 0.4)^{20 - 10}$

   $P(X = 10) = \binom{20}{10}0.4^{10}(0.6)^{10}$

            $= 0.1171$ (correct to 4 s.f.)

> The binomial distribution B(20, 0.4) is used here. The probability $p = 0.4$ is too high for the Poisson distribution to be used where ideally p should be less than 0.1. Also, n should be > 50.

  (ii) $P(X > 7) = 1 - P(X \leq 7)$

         $= 1 - 0.4159$

         $= 0.5841$

> To find P(X ≤ 7) we use the tables for the binomial distribution function with $n = 20, p = 0.4$ and $x = 7$.

(b) $\lambda = np = 300 \times 0.05 = 15$

   X is distributed as Po(15)

   $P(X < 10) = P(X \leq 9) = 0.0699$

> Tables should be used here as using the formula would be tedious because you would have 10 individual probabilities to calculate before adding them together.

Test yourself (using RND Tables)

1 It is known that 25% of the bulbs in a box produce yellow flowers. A customer buys 20 of these bulbs. Find the probability that:

(a) exactly 4 bulbs produce yellow flowers

(b) fewer than 8 bulbs produce yellow flowers.

2 The number of items of junk mail arriving by post each day at a house can be modelled by a Poisson distribution with mean 3.4.

(a) Without using tables, calculate:

(i) $P(X = 4)$

(ii) $P(X \leq 2)$.

(b) Using tables, determine

$P(4 \leq X \leq 7)$.

3 The random variable X has the binomial distribution B (20, 0.25).

Given that $Y = 4X - 2$, calculate

(a) $E(Y)$,

(b) $Var(Y)$,

(c) $P(Y = 10)$.

4 Each time a dart player throws a dart at the bulls-eye they hit the bulls-eye with a probability 0.08. The dart player throws 100 darts at the bulls-eye. Use a Poisson approximation to find the probability that she hits the bulls-eye fewer than 5 times.

Q & A

1

1 (a) A series of trials is carried out, each resulting in either success or failure. State **two** conditions that have to be satisfied in order for the total number of successes to be modelled by the binomial distribution. [2]

   (b) Each time Ann shoots an arrow at a target, she hits it with probability 0·4. She shoots 20 arrows at the target. Determine the probability that she hits it:

   (i)   exactly 8 times

   (ii) between 6 and 10 times (both inclusive). [5]

   (c) Each time she shoots an arrow, she hits the centre of the target with probability 0·04. She shoots 100 arrows at the target. Use a Poisson approximation to find the probability that she hits the centre of the target fewer than 5 times. [3]

   (WJEC S1 June 2011 Q7)

Answer

1 (a) The two conditions are:

   ▪ independent trials,

   ▪ trials where there is a constant probability of success.

   (b) (i) $P(X = x) = \binom{n}{x}p^x(1 - p)^{n - x}$

      Now $p = 0.4$, $n = 20$, $x = 8$, so we have

      $P(X = 8) = \binom{20}{8}0.4^8(1 - 0.4)^{20 - 8}$

      $P(X = 8) = \binom{20}{8}0.4^8(0.6)^{12}$

      $= 0.1787$ (correct to 4 s.f.)

      (ii) $P(6 \leq X \leq 10) = P(X \leq 10) - P(X \leq 5)$

         $= 0.8725 - 0.1256$

         $= 0.7469$ (correct to 4 s.f.)

   (c) Mean, $\lambda = np = 100 \times 0.04 = 4$

      The number of hits, X, is approximately Po(4).

      $P(X < 5) = P(X \leq 4) = 0.6288$ (correct to 4 s.f.)

Grade boost

Questions on the conditions for which a certain modelling formula can be used are frequent. Make sure you remember the conditions for each formula you use.

The formula is obtained from the formula booklet.

$P(X = 8) = P(X \leq 8) - P(X \leq 7)$

$= 0.5956 - 0.4159$

$= 0.1797$ (correct to 4 s.f.)

The Poisson distribution function tables are used to look up the $P(X \leq x)$ values. Using the tables the probability corresponding to values $x = 4$ and $\lambda = 4$ is looked up.

Q&A 2

2 Wine glasses are packed in boxes, each containing 20 glasses. Each glass has a probability of 0·05 of being broken in transit, independently of all other glasses.

(a) Let X denote the number of glasses in a box broken in transit.

   (i)   State the distribution of X.

   (ii) **Without** the use of tables, calculate P($X = 1$).

   (iii) **Using tables**, determine the value of P($X = 3$).   [5]

(b) A retailer buys 10 of these boxes. Use a Poisson approximation to find the probability that fewer than 5 of the 200 glasses are broken in transit.   [3]

(WJEC S1 Jan 2011 Q8)

Answer

2 (a) (i) The distribution is B (20, 0.05)

   (ii) P($X = 1$) = $\binom{20}{1}0.05^1(1 - 0.05)^{20-1}$

                   = $\binom{20}{1}0.05^1(0.95)^{19}$

                   = 0.377 (correct to 3 s.f.)

   (iii) P($X \geq 3$) = 1 – P($X \leq 2$) = 1 – 0.9245

                        = 0.0755

(b) Mean $\lambda = np = 200 \times 0.05 = 10$

   X is Po(10)

   P($X < 5$) = P($X \leq 4$) = 0.0293

> This is a binomial distribution because n is small and would need to be >50 to use the Poisson distribution. Hence we insert $n = 20$ and $p = 0.05$ into B (n, p) to give B (20, 0.05).

> Use the formula P($X = x$) = $\binom{n}{x}p^x(1 - p)^{n-x}$ obtained from the formula booklet.

> Use the cumulative Poisson probabilities table to find P($X \leq 4$).
> Use the table with $n = 20$, $p = 0.05$ and $x = 4$.

Q&A

3

3 When seeds of a certain variety of flower are planted, the probability of each seed germinating is 0·8, independently of all other seeds.

(a) David plants 20 of these seeds. Find the probability that:

    (i)   exactly 15 seeds germinate

    (ii) at least 15 seeds germinate.   [6]

(b) Beti plants n of these seeds and she correctly calculates that the probability that they all germinate is 0.10737, correct to five decimal places. Find the value of n.   [3]

(WJEC S1 Jan 2010 Q5)

Answer

3 (a) (i) Distribution is B(20, 0.8)

$$P(X = 15) = \binom{20}{15}0.8^{15}(1 - 0.8)^5$$

$$= 0.1746$$

> **Or** Let Y = no. of seeds failing to germinate.
>
> Y is distributed as B(20, 0.2)
>
> $P(X = 15) = P(Y = 5)$
> $$= P(Y \le 5) - P(Y \le 4)$$
> $$= 0.8042 - 0.6296$$
> $$= 0.1746$$

      (ii) Let the number of seeds failing to germinate = Y.

           Y is distributed as B(20, 0.2)

           $P(X \ge 15) = P(Y \le 5) = 0.8042$

> Use the binomial cumulative distribution function table with $n = 20$, $p = 0.2$ and $x = 5$. Read off the probability which is 0.8042.

(b) Distribution is B(n, 0.8)

$$P(X = n) = \binom{n}{n}0.8^n(1 - 0.8)^0$$

$$0.10737 = 0.8^n$$

Taking $\log_e$ of both sides, we obtain

$$\log_e 0.10737 = \log_e 0.8^n$$

so $\log_e 0.10737 = n\log_e 0.8$

$$n = \frac{\log_e 0.10737}{\log_e 0.8}$$

Hence, $n = 10$

> Note that you could also take logarithms of both sides to base 10 to solve this equation.

> Note that as n is the number of seeds germinating, n has to be an integer.

Summary: Binomial and Poisson distributions

For a fixed number of trials, n, each with a probability p of occurring, the probability of a number x of successes is given by the formula:

$$P(X = x) = \binom{n}{x} p^x (1 - p)^{n - x}$$

Conditions for using the binomial distribution

The conditions for using the binomial distribution are:

- Independent trials (i.e where the probability of one event does not depend on another)
- Trials where there is a constant probability of success
- A fixed number of trials
- Where there is only success or failure

The mean and variance of the binomial distribution

If X is B (n, p) then, Mean = np and Variance Var$(X) = np(1 - p)$

The standard deviation, σ, is related to the variance by the following equation:

$$\sigma^2 = \text{Var}(X) \text{ so } \sigma = \sqrt{\text{Var}(X)}$$

The Poisson distribution

In a particular interval, the probability of an event X occurring x number of times is given by the following formula:

$$P(X = x) = e^{-\lambda} \frac{\lambda^x}{x!} \quad \text{where } \lambda = \mu = E(X) \text{ and } x = 0, 1, 2, 3, 4, \ldots$$

Mean and variance of the Poisson distribution

If X is Po(λ) then,

Mean, $\mu = \lambda$

Variance $= \lambda$

Using the Poisson distribution to approximate the binomial distribution

In general we can approximate the binomial distribution by using the Poisson distribution in the following circumstances:

If n is large (usually > 50) and

p is small (usually <0.1).

Under these conditions, B(n, p) is approximated by Po (λ), where $\lambda = m = np$

Topic 4 — Continuous probability distributions

This topic covers the following:

- Continuous probability distributions
- Probability density and cumulative distribution functions and their relationships
- Medians, quartiles and percentiles
- Mean, variance and standard deviation
- Use of the results $E(aX + b) = aE(X) + b$ and $Var(aX + b) = a^2Var(X)$
- Expected value of a function of a continuous random variable

Continuous probability distributions

In Topic 2 you came across discrete probability distributions where the random variable X could only take isolated discrete values such as 1, 2, 3, 4, 5 and 6. With discrete probability distributions you could not have in-between values such as 1.001 or 2.5.

With continuous distributions all in-between numbers are possible as long as they lie inside a certain range.

Probability density and cumulative distribution functions and their relationships

The probability density function (p.d.f.)

The probability density function (p.d.f.) of a continuous random variable is a function that describes the relative likelihood for this random variable to take on a given value. In order to find the probability that the random variable falls within a particular region, you find the integral of the function over the region. If you integrate the probability function over the entire space, then it is equal to 1.

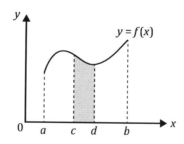

If $f(x)$ is defined for $a \leq x \leq b$ and we require the probability that x lies between and including c and d (i.e. $c \leq x \leq d$), then the probability function is integrated between these two limits. The required probability is therefore the area of the region bounded by the curve and the lines $x = c$ and $x = d$ which is shown shaded in the above graph.

Hence $\qquad P(c \leq x \leq d) = \int_{c}^{d} f(x)\, dx.$

As $f(x)$ is valid for $a \leq x \leq b$ the total area under the curve between $x = a$ and $x = b$ will be equal to 1.

Hence we have $\qquad \int_a^b f(x)\, dx = 1$

Examples

❶ The continuous random variable X has probability density function f given by

$f(x) = \frac{1}{6}(x + 1), \quad$ for $1 \leq x \leq 3,$

$f(x) = 0, \quad$ otherwise.

Calculate $P(1 \leq X \leq 2)$.

Answer

① $P(1 \leq X \leq 2) = \int_1^2 f(x)\, dx$

$\qquad = \frac{1}{6}\int_1^2 (x + 1)\, dx$

$\qquad = \frac{1}{6}\left[\frac{x^2}{2} + x\right]_1^2$

$\qquad = \frac{1}{6}\left[\left(2 + 2\right) - \left(\frac{1}{2} + 1\right)\right]$

$\qquad = \frac{5}{12}$

> The probability of a range of values can be found by finding the area between the values under a p.d.f curve. The integration of a p.d.f between the two values can be used to find this area.

❷ The continuous random variable X has probability density function f given by

$f(x) = kx(x - 1), \qquad$ for $1 \leq x \leq 2,$

$f(x) = 0, \qquad$ otherwise.

Prove that $k = \dfrac{6}{5}$.

Answer

② $\int_1^2 f(x) = 1$

Hence $\qquad k\int_1^2 x(x - 1) = 1$

$\qquad k\int_1^2 (x^2 - x)\, dx = 1$

$\qquad k\left[\frac{x^3}{3} - \frac{x^2}{2}\right]_1^2 = 1$

$k\left[\left(\frac{2^3}{3} - \frac{2^2}{2}\right) - \left(\frac{1^3}{3} - \frac{1^2}{2}\right)\right] = 1$

$k\left[\left(\frac{8}{3} - 2\right) - \left(\frac{1}{3} - \frac{1}{2}\right)\right] = 1$

$\qquad k\left[\frac{2}{3} - \left(-\frac{1}{6}\right)\right] = 1$

$\qquad \frac{5}{6}k = 1$

Hence $\qquad k = \dfrac{6}{5}$

> Before you put the p.d.f. equal to one, you must make sure that you are integrating between the limits of the allowable extreme values for the function.

> Note that it best to put the constant k outside the integral.

> Remember that to integrate you increase the index by one and then divide by this new index.

❸ The continuous random variable X has probability density function f given by

$f(x) = k(4 - x)$,   for $1 \leq x \leq 3$,

$f(x) = 0$,   otherwise.

(a) Calculate the value of k.

(b) Calculate $P(1 \leq X \leq 2)$.

Answer

③ (a) $\int_1^3 f(x)dx = 1$

$$k\int_1^3 (4 - x)dx = 1$$

$$k\left[4x - \frac{x^2}{2}\right]_1^3 = 1$$

$$k\left[\left(12 - \frac{9}{2}\right) - \left(4 - \frac{1}{2}\right)\right]_1^3 = 1$$

$$4k = 1$$

Hence, $k = \frac{1}{4}$

> Note that as the function is a p.d.f , when integrated over the whole allowable range, the answer will be one.

(b) $P(1 \leq X \leq 2) = \int_1^2 f(x)dx$

$$= \frac{1}{4}\left[4x - \frac{x^2}{2}\right]_1^2$$

$$= \frac{1}{4}\left[(8 - 2) - \left(4 - \frac{1}{2}\right)\right]$$

$$= 0.625$$

Expected value of a continuous random variable

For a continuous random variable X having probability density function f the expected value also called the mean (μ) or expectation $E(X)$ is given by:

Expectation (mean): $E(X) = \mu = \int xf(x)dx$

> This formula is included in the formula booklet.

so you multiply the p.d.f. by x and then integrate across the allowable range.

Examples

❶ The continuous random variable X has probability density function f given by

$f(x) = 20(x^3 - x^4)$,   for $0 \leq x \leq 1$,

$f(x) = 0$,   otherwise.

Find $E(X)$.

Answer

① $E(X) = \int_0^1 xf(x)\,dx$

$= \int_0^1 20x(x^3 - x^4)\,dx$

$= 20\int_0^1 (x^4 - x^5)\,dx$

$= 20\left[\dfrac{x^5}{5} - \dfrac{x^6}{6}\right]_0^1$

$= 20\left[\left(\dfrac{1}{5} - \dfrac{1}{6}\right) - \left(0 - 0\right)\right]$

$= \dfrac{2}{3}$

> The formula $E(X) = \mu = \int xf(x)\,dx$ is obtained from the formula booklet.

❷ The continuous random variable X has probability density function given by

$f(x) = \dfrac{3}{4}(x^2 + 1),$ for $0 \le x \le 1$,

$f(x) = 0,$ otherwise.

Find $E(X)$.

Answer

② $E(X) = \mu = \int xf(x)\,dx$

$E(X) = \int_0^1 x\dfrac{3}{4}(x^2 + 1)\,dx$

$E(X) = \dfrac{3}{4}\int_0^1 (x^3 + x)\,dx$

$= \dfrac{3}{4}\left[\dfrac{x^4}{4} + \dfrac{x^2}{2}\right]_0^1$

$= \dfrac{3}{4}\left[\left(\dfrac{1}{4} + \dfrac{1}{2}\right) - \left(0 + 0\right)\right]$

$= \dfrac{9}{16}$

> This formula is obtained from the formula booklet.

> Remember that to integrate you increase the index by 1 and then divide by this new index.

Variance and standard deviation for a continuous random variable

The variance of a continuous random variable X having probability density function f, is given by:

Variance: $\mathrm{Var}(X) = \sigma^2 = \int (x - \mu)^2 f(x)\,dx = \int x^2 f(x)\,dx - \mu^2$

where $\mu = E(X) =$ mean and $\sigma =$ standard deviation.

> Note that this formula is included in the formula booklet. Note also that the symbols such as μ and σ are not defined in the formula booklet so you need to remember what they mean.

Example

❶ The continuous random variable X has probability density function f given by

$f(x) = kx^2(3 - x),$ for $0 \le x \le 3,$

$f(x) = 0,$ otherwise.

(a) Calculate the value of k.

(b) Calculate the mean, μ.

(c) Calculate the variance and the standard deviation.

Answer

① (a) $\int_0^3 f(x)dx = 1$

$$\int_0^3 kx^2(3 - x)dx = 1$$

$$k\int_0^3 (3x^2 - x^3)dx = 1$$

$$k\left[\frac{3x^3}{3} - \frac{x^4}{4}\right]_0^3 = 1$$

$$k\left[\left(27 - \frac{81}{4}\right) - \left(0 - 0\right)\right] = 1$$

Solving, we obtain $k = \dfrac{4}{27} = 0.1481$ (correct to 4 d.p.)

(b) $\mu = \int xf(x)dx$

$$= \int_0^3 xkx^2(3 - x)dx$$

$$= k\int_0^3 x^3(3 - x)dx$$

$$= k\int_0^3 (3x^3 - x^4)dx$$

$$= k\left[\frac{3x^4}{4} - \frac{x^5}{5}\right]_0^3$$

$$= k\left[\frac{243}{4} - \frac{243}{5}\right]$$

$$= \frac{4}{27} \times \frac{243}{20} = 1.8$$

> The formula $E(X) = \mu = \int xf(x)dx$ is obtained from the formula booklet.

> It is convenient to take out the constant from the integration.

> The value of k is substituted into this expression.

(c) Variance: $Var(X) = \int x^2 f(x)dx - \mu^2$

$$= \int_0^3 x^2 kx^2(3 - x)dx - \mu^2$$

$$= k\int_0^3 (3x^4 - x^5)dx - \mu^2$$

$$= k\left[\frac{3x^5}{5} - \frac{x^6}{6}\right]_0^3 - \mu^2$$

$$= k\left[\frac{729}{5} - \frac{729}{6}\right] - \mu^2$$

$$= \frac{4}{27} \times \frac{729}{30} - 1.8^2$$

$$= 0.36$$

> μ is substituted from (b).

$$\text{Var}(X) = \sigma^2$$

Hence, standard deviation, $\sigma = \sqrt{\text{Var}(X)}$

$$= \sqrt{0.36}$$

$$= 0.6$$

The cumulative distribution function

The cumulative distribution function F(X) gives the probability that X is less than or equal to a certain value x and is given by the formula

$$F(x) = P(X \le x) = \int_{-\infty}^{x} f(t)dt$$

This formula for the cumulative distribution function (c.d.f.) for short is found in the formula booklet and need not be remembered.

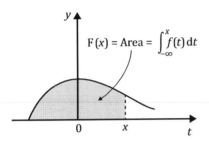

$$F(x) = \text{Area} = \int_{-\infty}^{x} f(t)\, dt$$

In this topic, we have used $-\infty$ as a lower limit to allow for all possibilities.

Notice the way the letter 't' has cropped up on the graph and in the formula for the cumulative distribution function. This is to avoid the confusion between the x in the function and the x used for the limit of integration.

Note that the cumulative distribution function is always written with a capital F to avoid confusion with the probability density function which is written with a lower case f.

Obtaining the cumulative distribution function F(x) from the probability density function f(x).

You saw in the previous section that

$$F(x) = P(X \le x) = \int_{-\infty}^{x} f(t)dt$$

Now suppose we have a probability density function which is valid for the range for $1 \le x \le 3$. As the smallest value x can take is no longer $-\infty$ but 1, we would integrate the p.d.f. between 1 and x, so the above equation for this instance would be:

Note that this formula can be obtained from the formula booklet.

$$F(x) = \int_{1}^{x} f(t)dt.$$

Examples

❶ The continuous random variable X has probability density function f given by

$$f(x) = 4 - 2x, \qquad \text{for } 1 \le x \le 2,$$

$$f(x) = 0, \qquad \text{otherwise.}$$

Show that for $1 \le x \le 2$, F(x) = $4x - x^2 - 3$

Answer

① $F(x) = \int_{-\infty}^{x} f(t)dt$

So, $F(x) = \int_{1}^{x} (4 - 2t)dt$

$= \left[4t - \dfrac{2t^2}{2}\right]_{1}^{x}$

$= [(4x - x^2) - (4 - 1)]$

$= 4x - x^2 - 3$

> Notice the 1 for the lower limit. This is because the lowest value x can take is 1. x the other limit can take any value up to including 2. We keep this limit as x because we want a general equation where any value in the range $1 \le x \le 2$ can be inserted for x.

❷ The continuous random variable X has probability density function f is given by

$f(x) = 20(x^3 - x^4)$ for $0 \le x \le 1$,

$f(x) = 0,$ otherwise.

Obtain an expression for $F(x)$, valid for $0 \le x \le 1$, where F denotes the cumulative distribution function of X.

Answer

② $F(x) = P(X \le x) = \int_{-\infty}^{x} f(t)dt$

So, $F(x) = \int_{0}^{x} 20(t^3 - t^4)dt$

$= 20\left[\dfrac{t^4}{4} - \dfrac{t^5}{5}\right]_{0}^{x}$

$= 20\left[\left(\dfrac{x^4}{4} - \dfrac{x^5}{5}\right) - \left(0 - 0\right)\right]$

$= 5x^4 - 4x^5$

> Note that this formula can be obtained from the formula booklet.

> Notice the way the variable x has been changed to t in order to prevent confusion with the x in the limits. Also the lower limit has been change from $-\infty$ to 0.

Obtaining the probability density function $f(x)$ from the cumulative distribution function $F(x)$

The probability density function $f(x)$ can be obtained from the cumulative distribution function $F(x)$ by differentiating the cumulative distribution function.

Hence, we have

$$f(x) = \dfrac{d}{dx}F(x)$$

Note that this can also be written as $f(x) = F'(x)$

> Note that this is not included in the formula booklet. You can remember this as being the reverse process of obtaining $F(x)$ from $f(x)$.

Examples

❶ The continuous random variable X has cumulative distribution function F given by

$F(x) = 4x^3 - 3x^4$ for $0 \le x \le 1$,

$F(x) = 0,$ otherwise.

Find the probability density function $f(x)$.

Answer

① $f(x) = \dfrac{d}{dx} F(x)$

$f(x) = \dfrac{d}{dx} (4x^3 - 3x^4)$

$\qquad = 12x^2 - 12x^3 \quad$ for $0 \le x \le 1$

and $f(x) = 0$, otherwise.

> Remember that when differentiating you multiply by the index and reduce the index by one.

❷ The continuous random variable X takes values between 1 and 2 and its cumulative distribution function F is given for $1 \le x \le 2$ by

$F(x) = ax^3 - bx^2$

Find the values of the constants a and b.

Answer

② $F(1) = a \times 1^3 - b \times 1^2 = a - b$

Now $F(1) = 0$, hence $a - b = 0$ $\hspace{2cm}$ (1)

$F(2) = a \times 2^3 - b \times 2^2 = 8a - 4b$

Now $F(2) = 1$, hence $8a - 4b = 1$ $\hspace{1.5cm}$ (2)

Solving equations (1) and (2) simultaneously gives

$a = \frac{1}{4}$ and $b = \frac{1}{4}$

> The two extreme values are chosen to be substituted into the equation for F(x) as F(1) = 0 and F(2) =1.

Medians, quartiles and percentiles

If X is a continuous random variable with a cumulative distribution function $F(x)$ then we have the following equations for the median, quartiles and percentiles:

The median, m, of X is given by $F(m) = 0.5$

The lower quartile, q_1, of X is given by $F(q_1) = 0.25$

The upper quartile, q_3, of X is given by $F(q_3) = 0.75$

The lowest percentile, p, of X is given by $F(p) = \dfrac{1}{100} = 0.01$

The largest percentile, p, of X is given by $F(p) = \dfrac{99}{100} = 0.99$

> Note that none of these results are included in the formula booklet. You will need to remember them.

Examples

❶ The continuous random variable X has cumulative distribution function F given by

$F(x) = 0 \qquad$ for $x < 0$,

$F(x) = 4x^3 - 3x^4 \quad$ for $0 \le x \le 1$,

$F(x) = 1 \qquad$ for $x > 1$.

(a) Evaluate $P(0.5 \le X \le 0.8)$.

(b) Calculate $F(0.4)$ and determine whether 0.4 is greater or less than the median.

Answer

① (a) $P(0.5 \leq X \leq 0.8) = P(x \leq 0.8) - P(x \leq 0.5) = F(0.8) - F(0.5)$

$= (4 \times 0.8^3 - 3 \times 0.8^4) - (4 \times 0.5^3 - 3 \times 0.5^4)$

$= 0.5067$

> The values 0.5 and 0.8 are substituted into the equation $F(x) = 4x^3 - 3x^4$.

(b) Now $F(0.4) = 4 \times 0.4^3 - 3 \times 0.4^4 = 0.1792$

Since $F(0.4) = 0.1792 < 0.5$, 0.4 is less than the median.

> You need to remember the result $F(m) = 0.5$.

❷ The continuous random variable X has probability density function f given by

$f(x) = \dfrac{x}{4}$, for $1 \leq x \leq 3$,

$f(x) = 0$, otherwise.

Find the median.

Answer

② $\displaystyle\int_1^m \dfrac{x}{4}\,dx = \dfrac{1}{2}$

> Between the lowest value (i.e. 1) and the median, m, the area under the curve must be half of the total area of 1. Hence the area is equal to $\frac{1}{2}$.

$\left[\dfrac{x^2}{8}\right]_1^m = \dfrac{1}{2}$

$\dfrac{m^2}{8} - \dfrac{1}{8} = \dfrac{1}{2}$

> Multiply through by 8 to remove the denominator.

$m^2 - 1 = 4$

$m^2 = 5$

$m = \pm\sqrt{5}$ The median cannot be $-\sqrt{5}$ so this solution is ignored.

Hence median $= \sqrt{5} = 2.2361$ (correct to 4 decimal places)

Use of the results $E(aX + b) = aE(X) + b$ and $Var(aX + b) = a^2Var(X)$

Here are the results for the expected value and variance for a continuous variable X.

$E(aX + b) = aE(X) + b$,

$Var(aX + b) = a^2Var(X)$.

where a and b are constants and X is the variable.

> Both of these equations are included in the formula booklet.

Example

❶ Given that $E(X) = 3$ and $Var(X) = 6$, calculate

(a) $E(2X - 1)$

(b) $Var(4X - 3)$

Answer

① (a) $E(aX + b) = aE(X) + b$

> This equation is given in the formula booklet.

Now $a = 2$ and $b = -1$, so

$E(2X - 1) = 2E(X) - 1$

Since $E(X) = 3$, $E(2X - 1) = 2 \times 3 - 1 = 5$

(b) $Var(aX + b) = a^2Var(X)$

> This equation is given in the formula booklet.

$Var(4X - 3) = 4^2Var(X) = 16 \times 6 = 96$

Expected value of a function of a continuous random variable

The expected value of a function of a continuous random variable is obtained using the following equation:

$$E(g(X)) = \int g(x)f(x)dx$$

> This formula is included in the formula booklet and need not be remembered.

Note that $g(X)$ is a simple function of X such as $\sqrt{X}, X^2, \dfrac{1}{X}$, etc.

Examples

❶   The continuous random variable X has probability density function given by

$f(x) = \frac{1}{2}x$ for $0 \leq x \leq 2$

$f(x) = 0$ otherwise

Calculate

(a) $E(X)$

(b) $E(X^2)$

Answer

① (a) $E(X) = \int x f(x)dx$

$E(X) = \int_0^2 x\left(\frac{1}{2}x\right)dx$

> This formula is included in the formula booklet.

$= \int_0^2 \left(\frac{x^2}{2}\right)dx$

$= \left[\frac{x^3}{6}\right]_0^2$

$= \left[\left(\frac{8}{6}\right) - (0)\right]$

$= \frac{4}{3}$ or 1.3333 (correct to 4 d.p.)

(b) $E(g(X)) = \int g(x)f(x)dx$

Now $g(x) = x^2$

Hence $E(g(X)) = \int_0^2 x^2f(x)dx$

> This formula is obtained from the formula booklet.

$= \int_0^2 x^2\left(\frac{1}{2}x\right)dx$

$$= \int_0^2 \frac{1}{2}x^3 dx$$

$$= \left[\frac{x^4}{8}\right]_0^2$$

$$= \left[\left(\frac{2^4}{8}\right) - (0)\right]$$

$$= 2$$

❷ The continuous random variable X has cumulative distribution function F given by

$\quad$ F$(x) = 0$ $\qquad\qquad$ for $x < 1$,

$\quad$ F$(x) = \frac{1}{10}\left(x^2 + x - 2\right)$ $\qquad$ for $1 \le x \le 3$,

$\quad$ F$(x) = 1$ $\qquad\qquad$ for $x > 3$.

(a) (i) Evaluate P$(2 \le X \le 2.5)$.

$\quad$ (ii) Find the median of X. $\hfill$ [7]

(b) (i) Obtain an expression for $f(x)$, valid for $1 \le x \le 3$, where f denotes the probability density function of X.

$\quad$ (ii) Write down the value of $f(4)$.

$\quad$ (iii) Calculate E(X). $\hfill$ [7]

$\hfill$ (WJEC S1 Jan 2010 Q8)

Answer

② (a) (i) $\quad$ P$(2 \le X \le 2·5) =$ F$(2.5) -$ F(2)

$$= \frac{1}{10}\left(2.5^2 + 2.5 - 2\right) - \frac{1}{10}\left(2^2 + 2 - 2\right)$$

$$= 0.275$$

> The two values $x = 2$ and $x = 2.5$ are substituted into the cumulative distribution function. As both results give the cumulative probabilities, F(2.5) – F(2) gives the required probability.

$\quad$ (ii) If the median value is m then

$$\text{F}(m) = \frac{1}{10}\left(m^2 + m - 2\right)$$

Now F$(m) = 0.5$ so we have $\frac{1}{10}\left(m^2 + m - 2\right) = 0.5$

Hence $m^2 + m - 7 = 0$

Using the formula $m = \dfrac{-b \pm \sqrt{b^2 - 4ac}}{2a}$

$$m = \frac{-1 \pm \sqrt{1^2 + 28}}{2}$$

$$m = 2.19$$

> m is substituted into the cumulative distribution function and this is equated to 0.5 as this is the probability associated with the median value.

> Note there is another solution, but it is negative and outside the range $1 \le x \le 3$ and so is ignored.

(b) (i) Probability density function, $f(x) =$ F$'(x)$

$$= \frac{1}{10}\left(2x + 1\right) \text{ for } 1 \le x \le 3$$

> Note that the cumulative distribution function is differentiated to obtain the p.d.f.

$\quad$ (ii) F$(x) = 1$ for $x > 3$ so as $f(x) =$ F$'(x)$,

$\qquad f(4) = 0$

> When 1 is differentiated you obtain 0.

$\quad$ (iii) E$(X) = \int_1^3 x f(x) dx$

$$= \int_1^3 \frac{1}{10}x(2x + 1)dx$$

> The formula Expectation (mean): E$(x) = \mu = \int x f(x)dx$ is looked up in the formula booklet.

$$= \frac{1}{10} \int_1^3 (2x^2 + x) \, dx$$

$$= \frac{1}{10} \left[\frac{2x^3}{3} + \frac{x^2}{2} \right]_1^3$$

$$= \frac{1}{10} \left[\left(\frac{2 \times 3^3}{3} + \frac{3^2}{2} \right) - \left(\frac{2 \times 1^3}{3} + \frac{1^2}{2} \right) \right]$$

$$= 2.13 \text{ (correct to 2 decimal places)}$$

❸ The continuous random variable X has probability density function f given by

$$f(x) = kx(1 - x^2), \qquad \text{for } 0 \le x \le 1,$$
$$f(x) = 0, \qquad \text{otherwise.}$$

where k is a constant.

(a) Show that $k = 4$.   [3]

(b) Calculate $E(X)$.   [4]

(c) (i)   Find an expression for $F(x)$, valid for $0 \le x \le 1$, where F denotes the cumulative distribution function of X.

  (ii) Evaluate $P(0.25 \le X \le 0.75)$.

  (iii) Find the median of X.   [9]

(WJEC S1 June 2010 Q8)

Answer

③ (a) $\int_0^1 f(x) \, dx = 1$

> Here we use the fact that the integral of the p.d.f. over the whole range of allowable values is equal to 1.

$$\int_0^1 kx(1 - x^2) \, dx = 1$$

$$k \int_0^1 (x - x^3) \, dx = 1$$

$$k \left[\frac{x^2}{2} - \frac{x^4}{4} \right]_0^1 = 1$$

$$k \left[\left(\frac{1^2}{2} - \frac{1^4}{4} \right) - (0 - 0) \right] = 1$$

Solving, we obtain $k = 4$

(b) $E(X) = \int_0^1 f(x) \, dx$

> This formula is obtained from the formula booklet.

$$= \int_0^1 x 4x(1 - x^2) \, dx$$

$$= \int_0^1 (4x^2 - 4x^4) \, dx$$

$$= \left[\frac{4x^3}{3} - \frac{4x^5}{5} \right]_0^1$$

$$= \left[\left(\frac{4}{3} - \frac{4}{5} \right) - (0 - 0) \right]$$

$$= \frac{8}{15}$$

(c) (i) $F(x) = P(X \le x) = \int_{-\infty}^{x} f(t)dt$

$$= \int_{0}^{x} 4t(1 - t^2)dt$$

$$= \int_{0}^{x} (4t - 4t^3)dt$$

$$= \left[2t^2 - t^4\right]_{0}^{x}$$

$$= 2x^2 - x^4 \quad \text{for } 0 \le x \le 1$$

The expression used here for the cumulative distribution function is obtained from the formula booklet.

Notice that the smallest value t can take is 0, so this is taken as the lower limit.

(ii) $P(0.25 \le X \le 0.75) = F(0.75) - F(0.25)$

$$= (2 \times 0.75^2 - 0.75^4) - (2 \times 0.25^2 - 0.25^4)$$

$$= 0.6875 \text{ (correct to 4 decimal places)}$$

The two values are substituted into the expression for the cumulative distribution function (i.e. $2x^2 - x^4$).

(iii) $F(m) = 0.5$

$$2m^2 - m^4 = 0.5$$

$$2m^4 - 4m^2 + 1 = 0$$

Let $x = m^2$

Hence $2x^2 - 4x + 1 = 0$

Solving using the formula gives

$$x = \frac{4 \pm \sqrt{8}}{4}$$

Multiply through by 2 so that only whole numbers appear in the equation.

This is done so that a quadratic equation in x is obtained which can then be solved using the formula.

Giving $x = 1.7071$ or 0.2929

Then $m = \sqrt{x} = 1.307$ or 0.541 (correct to 3 decimal places).

The value 1.307 is ignored because it lies outside the range $[0, 1]$.

Hence $m = 0.541$ (correct to 3 decimal places).

Examination style questions

1 A small shop sells olive oil from a barrel. The store owner finds that during the autumn the daily demand for olive oil, X, may be regarded as a continuous random variable with probability density function f given by

$f(x) = kx^2(10 - x)$,   for $0 \le x \le 10$,

$f(x) = 0$,   otherwise.

(a) Verify that $k = 0.0012$.

(b) Find the mean and the standard deviation of the distribution.

Answer

① (a) $\int_0^{10} f(x)\,dx = 1$

$$\int_0^{10} kx^2(10 - x)\,dx = 1$$

$$k\int_0^{10} (10x^2 - x^3)\,dx = 1$$

> This works out the area under the graph between 0 and 10 and this is the total probability which will be equal to 1.

$$k\left[\frac{10x^3}{3} - \frac{x^4}{4}\right]_0^{10} = 1$$

$$k\left[\left(\frac{10\,000}{3} - \frac{10\,000}{4}\right) - (0 - 0)\right] = 1$$

Solving, we obtain $k = 0.0012$

Grade boost

Don't bother wasting time finding common denominators, etc. Instead work out the fractions using a calculator if the final answer is a decimal.

(b) Mean, $\mu = \int xf(x)\,dx$

$$= \int_0^{10} xkx^2(10 - x)\,dx$$

$$= k\int_0^{10} (10x^3 - x^4)\,dx$$

$$= k\left[\frac{10x^4}{4} - \frac{x^5}{5}\right]_0^{10}$$

$$= 0.0012\left[\left(\frac{100\,000}{4} - \frac{100\,000}{5}\right) - (0 - 0)\right]$$

$$= 6$$

> This formula is available in the formula booklet.

> Remember that to integrate you increase the index by 1 and then divide by this new index.

Variance: $\text{Var}(X) = \int x^2 f(x)\,dx - \mu^2$

$$= \int_0^{10} x^2 kx^2(10 - x)\,dx - \mu^2$$

$$= k\int_0^{10} (10x^4 - x^5)\,dx - 6^2$$

> This formula is available in the formula booklet.

> This formula is obtained from the formula booklet.

$$= 0.0012\left[\frac{10x^5}{5} - \frac{x^6}{6}\right]_0^{10} - 36$$

$$= 0.0012[(200\,000 - 166\,666.67) - (0 - 0)] - 36$$

$$= 4$$

Standard deviation, $\sigma = \sqrt{\text{Var}(X)} = \sqrt{4} = 2$

Test yourself

Answer the following questions and check your answers.

❶ The continuous random variable X has probability density function given by

$f(x) = \frac{1}{2}\sqrt{x} + \frac{2}{3}$,   for $0 \le x \le 1$,

$f(x) = 0$,   otherwise.

Calculate $E(\sqrt{x})$.

❷ The continuous random variable X has probability density function given by

$f(x) = k(4 - x)$,   for $-2 \le x \le 2$,

$f(x) = 0$,   otherwise.

(a) Calculate the value of the constant k.

(b) Calculate

   (i) $E(X)$,

   (ii) $P(-1 \le x \le 1)$.

❸ The continuous random variable X has cumulative distribution function F given by

$F(x) = 0$,   for $x \le 0$,

$F(x) = 5x^2 - 4x$ for $0 \le x \le 1$,

$F(x) = 1$ for $x > 1$.

(a) Evaluate $P(0.25 \le X \le 0.75)$.

(b) Obtain an expression for $f(x)$, valid for $0 \le x \le 1$, where $f(x)$ denotes the probability density function of X.

(c) Evaluate $E(X)$.

Q & A

1

---

1 (a) The continuous random variable X has probability density function f given by

$\qquad f(x) = 12x^2(1-x)$ for $0 \le x \le 1$,

$\qquad f(x) = 0$ otherwise.

Calculate

(i) $E(X)$

(ii) $E\left(\dfrac{1}{X}\right)$

(iii) $P(0.2 \le x \le 0.5)$. [9]

(b) The continuous random variable Y takes values between 1 and 2 and its cumulative distribution function F is given, for $1 \le y \le 2$, by

$\qquad F(y) = ay + by^2$.

Find the values of the constants a and b. [4]

(WJEC S1 June 2011 Q8)

Answer

1 (a) (i) $E(X) = \mu = \int xf(x)dx$

$\qquad E(X) = \int_0^1 12x^2 x(1-x)dx$

> This formula is obtained from the formula booklet.

$\qquad = \int_0^1 (12x^3 - 12x^4)dx$

$\qquad = \left[\dfrac{12x^4}{4} - \dfrac{12x^5}{5}\right]_0^1$

$\qquad = [(3 - 2.4) - (0 - 0)]$

$\qquad = 0.6$

(ii) $E\left(\dfrac{1}{X}\right) = \int_0^1 \dfrac{12}{x} x^2(1-x)dx$

> Here we use the formula $E(g(X)) = \int g(x)f(x)dx$ which is looked up in the formula booklet.

$\qquad = \int_0^1 12x(1-x)dx$

$\qquad = \int_0^1 (12x - 12x^2)dx$

$\qquad = \left[\dfrac{12x^2}{2} - \dfrac{12x^3}{3}\right]_0^1$

$\qquad = [(6 - 4) - (0 - 0)]$

$\qquad = 2$

(iii) $P(0.2 \le X \le 0.5) = \int_{0.2}^{0.5} f(x)dx$

$\qquad = \int_{0.2}^{0.5} 12x^2(1-x)dx$

$\qquad = \left[\dfrac{12x^3}{3} - \dfrac{12x^4}{4}\right]_{0.2}^{0.5}$

$\qquad = 0.285$ (correct to 3 decimal places)

(b) $F(y) = ay + by^2$

When $y = 1$, $F(1) = 0$.

Hence, $0 = a + b$ (1)

When $y = 2$, $F(2) = 1$.

Hence, $1 = 2a + 4b$ (2)

Solving equations (1) and (2) simultaneously we obtain

$a = -\frac{1}{2}, b = \frac{1}{2}$

Q&A 2

2   The continuous random variable X has cumulative distribution function F given by

$F(x) = 0$ for $x < 1$,

$F(x) = \frac{1}{5}(x^2 + 2x - 3)$ for $1 \leq x \leq 2$,

$F(x) = 1$ for $x > 2$.

(a)   (i)   Evaluate $P(1.2 \leq X \leq 1.5)$.

    (ii)   Find the median of X.   [7]

(b)   (i)   Obtain an expression for $f(x)$, valid for $1 \leq x \leq 2$, where f denotes the probability density function of X.

    (ii)   Calculate $E(X)$.   [7]

Answer

2   (a)   (i) $P(1.2 \leq X \leq 1.5) = F(1.5) - F(1.2)$

$$= \frac{1}{5}\left[(1.5^2 + 2 \times 1.5 - 3) - (1.2^2 + 2 \times 1.2 - 3)\right]$$

$$= 0.282$$

(ii)   The median m is given by

$F(m) = 0.5$

Now $F(m) = \frac{1}{5}\left(m^2 + 2m - 3\right) = 0.5$

$m^2 + 2m - 3 = 2.5$

$m^2 + 2m - 5.5 = 0$

Multiplying by 2 we obtain

$2m^2 + 4m - 11 = 0$

Hence, $m = \dfrac{-4 \pm \sqrt{16 + 88}}{4}$

$m = \dfrac{-4 \pm \sqrt{104}}{4}$

$m = -3.55, 1.55$

> You need to recognise that this cannot be factorised easily so it needs to be solved using the quadratic formula. Note that the formula for solving quadratic equations is not included in the formula booklet and will need to be remembered.

> Note that the negative solution is ignored as the median in this case cannot be negative.

Since the value of m must be between 1 and 2, $m = 1.55$ (correct to 2 decimal places).

(b) (i) $f(x) = F'(x)$

$\qquad = \frac{1}{5}\left(2x + 2\right) \qquad$ for $1 \le x \le 2$.

Note that this formula is not
included in the formula booklet.

(ii) $E(X) = \displaystyle\int_{1}^{2} x f(x)\,\mathrm{d}x$

$\qquad = \displaystyle\int_{1}^{2} x\frac{1}{5}\left(2x + 2\right)\mathrm{d}x$

$\qquad = \frac{1}{5}\displaystyle\int_{1}^{2}\left(2x^2 + 2x\right)\mathrm{d}x$

$\qquad = \frac{1}{5}\left[\frac{2x^3}{3} + x^2\right]_{1}^{2}$

$\qquad = \frac{1}{5}\left[\left(\frac{16}{3} + 4\right) - \left(\frac{2}{3} + 1\right)\right]$

$\qquad = 1.53$ (correct to two decimal places)

Summary: Continuous probability distributions

The probability density function (p.d.f.)

If $f(x)$ is a probability density function, then
$$P(c \leq x \leq d) = \int_c^d f(x)dx$$
Also, if a and b are the extreme values over which the p.d.f. is valid then
$$\int_a^b f(x) = 1$$

Expected value for a continuous random variable

For a continuous random variable X having probability density function f, the expected value also called the mean (μ) or expectation ($E(X)$) is given by:

Expectation (mean): $\quad E(X) = \mu = \int xf(x)dx$

Variance and standard deviation for a continuous random variable

The variance of a continuous random variable X having probability density function f, is given by:

Variance: $\quad Var(X) = \sigma^2 = \int (x_i - \mu)^2 f(x)dx = \int x^2 f(x)dx - \mu^2$

where $\mu = E(X)$ = mean and σ = standard deviation.

The cumulative distribution function

The cumulative distribution function $F(X)$ gives the probability that X is less than or equal to a certain value x and is given by the formula
$$F(x) = P(X \leq x) = \int_{-\infty}^x f(t)dt$$

Obtaining the probability density function $f(x)$ from the cumulative distribution function $F(x)$

$$f(x) = \frac{d}{dx} F(x)$$

Note that this can also be written as $f(x) = F'(x)$

Medians, quartiles and percentiles

If X is a continuous random variable with a cumulative distribution function $F(x)$, then we have the following equations for the median, quartiles and percentiles:

The median, m, of X is given by $F(m) = 0.5$

The lower quartile, q_1, of X is given by $F(q_1) = 0.25$

The upper quartile, q_3, of X is given by $F(q_3) = 0.75$

The percentile, p, of X is given by $F(p) = \dfrac{p}{100}$

Use of the results $E(aX + b) = aE(X) + b$ and $Var(aX + b) = a^2Var(X)$

The following results for the expected value and variance have the same equations for a continuous variable X as it had for a discrete variable X covered in Topic 2.

$$E(aX + b) = aE(X) + b$$
$$Var(aX + b) = a^2Var(X)$$

where a and b are constants and X is the variable.

Expected value of a function of a continuous random variable

The expected value of a function of a continuous random variable is obtained using the following equation:

$$E(g(X)) = \int g(x)f(x)dx$$

Test yourself answers

Topic 1 Probability

① (a) Probability of event A only = 0.45 – 0.25 = 0.2

Probability of event B only = 0.30 – 0.25 = 0.05

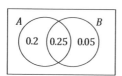

The probability of event A only is found by subtracting the probability of P($A \cap B$) from P(A). The probability of B only is also found by subtracting P($A \cap B$) from P(B).

A Venn diagram showing these probabilities and the probability of $A \cap B$ can now be drawn.

P($A \cup B$) = 0.2 + 0.25 + 0.05 = 0.5

Alternatively, you could use

P($A \cup B$) = P(A) + P(B) – P($A \cap B$)

= 0.45 + 0.30 – 0.25

= 0.5

(b) P($A' \cap B'$) = 1 – 0.5 = 0.5

$A' \cap B'$ represents everything outside $A \cup B$. Note that the probability of both of these events adds up to 1. Hence, P($A' \cap B'$) = 1 – P($A \cup B$).

(c) $P(B|A') = \dfrac{P(B \cap A')}{P(A')} = \dfrac{0.05}{0.55} = \dfrac{1}{11}$

P(A') = 0.5 + 0.05 = 0.55 or P(A') = 1 – P(A) = 0.55

② (a) Probability of three yellow counters $= \dfrac{4}{9} \times \dfrac{3}{8} \times \dfrac{2}{7} = \dfrac{1}{21}$

Or $\dfrac{^4C_3}{^9C_3} = \dfrac{4}{84} = \dfrac{1}{21}$

(b) Probability of no blue counters $= \dfrac{6}{9} \times \dfrac{5}{8} \times \dfrac{4}{7} = \dfrac{5}{21}$

Or $\dfrac{^6C_3}{^9C_3} = \dfrac{20}{84} = \dfrac{5}{21}$

(c) Probability of one counter of each colour $= 6 \times \dfrac{2}{9} \times \dfrac{3}{8} \times \dfrac{4}{7} = \dfrac{2}{7}$

③ (a) P(two red) $= \dfrac{2}{10} \times \dfrac{1}{9} = \dfrac{2}{90}$

P(two blue) $= \dfrac{3}{10} \times \dfrac{2}{9} = \dfrac{6}{90}$

P(two yellow) $= \dfrac{5}{10} \times \dfrac{4}{9} = \dfrac{20}{90}$

Or $\dfrac{^2C_1 \times {}^3C_1 \times {}^4C_1}{^9C_3} = \dfrac{2 \times 3 \times 4}{84} = \dfrac{2}{7}$

P(two the same colour) = P(two red) + P(two blue) + P(two yellow)

$= \dfrac{2}{90} + \dfrac{6}{90} + \dfrac{20}{90}$

$= \dfrac{28}{90}$

$= \dfrac{14}{45}$

Or $\dfrac{^2C_2 + {}^3C_2 + {}^5C_2}{^{10}C_2} = \dfrac{1 + 3 + 10}{45} = \dfrac{14}{45}$

(b) P(two different colours) = 1 – P(two the same colour)

$= 1 - \dfrac{14}{45}$

$= \dfrac{31}{45}$

④ (a) (i) When throwing two dice, the sample space consists of 36 pairs of scores.

The number of pairs the same = 6

Hence, P(scores are equal) = 6/36 = 1/6

> The pairs the same are (1,1), (2, 2), (3, 3), (4, 4), (5,5) and (6, 6).

(ii) The possible scores where Amy's score is higher are:

(2, 1)

(3, 1), (3, 2)

(4, 1), (4, 2), (4, 3)

(5, 1), (5, 2), (5, 3), (5, 4)

(6, 1), (6, 2), (6, 3), (6, 4), (6, 5)

> All the possible scores where Amy's score is higher than Bethany's score are listed. Here it is assumed that Amy throws first so the pairs are listed in the order (A, B).

Hence, Probability that Amy's score is higher $= \dfrac{15}{36} = \dfrac{5}{12}$

(b) Sample space consists of:

(1, 3), (3, 1), (2, 2)

Probability scores are equal $= \dfrac{1}{3}$

> Note that the sample space is now reduced from 36 to only 3 of which there is only one pair the same giving a total of 4 (i.e. (2, 2)).

⑤ (a) Using $P(A \cup B) = P(A) + P(B) - P(A \cap B)$ and $P(A \cap B) = P(A) \times P(B)$, we obtain

$$0.5 = 0.3 + P(B) - 0.3 \times P(B)$$

$$0.2 = 0.7\,P(B)$$

Hence, P(B) = 0.2857 (correct to 4 d.p.)

(b) P(exactly one event occurs) $= P(A \cup B) - P(A \cap B)$

$= 0.5 - 0.3 \times 0.2857$

$= 0.5 - 0.0857$

$= 0.4143$

> Note that $P(A \cap B) = P(A) \times P(B)$ as they are independent.

(c) P(B only occurs out of the two events|one event occurs)

$$= \dfrac{P(B) - P(A \cap B)}{0.4143} = \dfrac{0.2857 - 0.0857}{0.4143}$$

$= 0.483$ (correct to 3 d.p.)

> Note that the probability of B only is given by $P(B) - P(A \cap B)$.

⑥ (a)

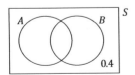

> Note that in drawing this Venn diagram we have assumed that there is an overlap between A and B. If the events are mutually exclusive then there would be no overlap.

From the Venn diagram, $P(A \cup B) = 1 - 0.4 = 0.6$

Using $P(A \cup B) = P(A) + P(B) - P(A \cap B)$,

we obtain $0.6 = 0.4 + 0.35 - P(A \cap B)$.

Hence, $P(A \cap B) = 0.15$ and as there is an overlap between events A and B, the two events are not mutually exclusive.

(b) $P(A) \times P(B) = 0.4 \times 0.35 = 0.14$, and as $P(A \cap B) = 0.15$, we have

$P(A) \times P(B) \neq P(A \cap B)$ proving that events A and B are not independent.

2 Discrete probability distributions

① (a)

x	1	2	3	4
$P(X = x)$	$4k$	$3k$	$2k$	k

Now $4k + 3k + 2k + k = 1$,

so $10k = 1$, giving $k = \frac{1}{10}$.

(b) $E(X) = \mu = \sum x_i p_i$

$$= \frac{1}{10}\left(1 \times 4 + 2 \times 3 + 3 \times 2 + 4 \times 1\right) = 2$$

$$E(X)^2 = \frac{1}{10}\left(1^2 \times 4 + 2^2 \times 3 + 3^2 \times 2 + 4^2 \times 1\right)$$

$$= \frac{1}{10}\left(1 \times 4 + 4 \times 3 + 9 \times 2 + 16 \times 1\right) = 5$$

$$\text{Var}(X) = E(X)^2 - \mu^2 = 5 - 2^2 = 1$$

② (a) $E(aX + b) = aE(X) + b$

$E(2X + 1) = 2E(X) + 1$

Now, $E(X) = 4$, so we have

$E(2X + 1) = 2 \times 4 + 1 = 9$

Hence $E(Y) = 9$

$\text{Var}(aX + b) = a^2\text{Var}(X)$

$\text{Var}(Y) = \text{Var}(2X + 1) = 2^2\text{Var}(X) = 4 \times 2 = 8$

> This formula is obtained from the formula booklet. Remember that $\mu = E(X)$. The random variable is changed from X to Y and the equation is rearranged.

(b) Now $\text{Var}(X) = E(X)^2 - \mu^2$

so $E(X)^2 = \text{Var}(X) + \mu^2$

Similarly $E(Y^2) = \text{Var}(Y) + \{E(Y)\}^2 = 8 + 81 = 89$

③ (a) $\sigma^2 = \text{Var}(X) = E(X)^2 - \mu^2$

$E(X^2) = \sum x_i^2 p_i = 1^2 \times 0.2 + 2^2 \times 0.4 + 3^2 \times 0.4 = 5.4$

$\sigma^2 = E(X)^2 - \mu^2 = 5.4 - 2.2^2 = 0.56$

> If you obtain the formula from the formula booklet and write it down you can see what quantities you need to find first to put into the formula

Hence standard deviation, $\sigma = \sqrt{0.56} = 0.748$ (correct to 3 d.p.)

(b) $E\left(\frac{1}{x}\right) = \frac{1}{1} \times 0.2 + \frac{1}{2} \times 0.4 + \frac{1}{3} \times 0.4$

$$= 0.533 \text{ (correct to 3 d.p.)}$$

④ (a)

x	2	4	6
$P(X = x)$	$2k$	$4k$	$6k$

> $\frac{1}{x}$ is found for each value of x and then it is multiplied by the probability. The results are then added together.

Now $2k + 4k + 6k = 1$,

so $12k = 1$, giving $k = \frac{1}{12}$.

(b) (i) $E(X) = \mu = \sum x_i p_i$

$$= \frac{1}{12}\left(2 \times 2 + 4 \times 4 + 6 \times 6\right) = 4.667 \text{ (correct to 3 d.p.)}$$

(ii) $E\left(\frac{1}{x}\right) = \frac{1}{12}\left(\frac{1}{2} \times 2 + \frac{1}{4} \times 4 + \frac{1}{6} \times 6\right) = 0.25$

3 Binomial and Poisson distributions (RND Tables)

① (a) $P(X = x) = \binom{n}{x}p^x(1 - p)^{n - x}$

> The formula is obtained from the formula booklet.

$p = 0.25$ and $n = 20$.

$P(X = 4) = \binom{20}{4}0.25^4(1 - 0.25)^{20 - 4}$

$= \binom{20}{4}0.25^4(0.75)^{16}$

$= 0.1897$ (correct to 4 s.f.)

> By tables $P(X = 4) = P(X \le 4) - P(X \le 3)$
> $= 0.4148 - 0.2252 = 0.1896$

(b) The binomial distribution tables are used here with $n = 20$, $p = 0.25$ and $x = 7$.

P(fewer than 8 bulbs) $= P(X \le 7) = 0.8982$

② (a) (i) $P(X = 4) = e^{-3.4}\dfrac{3.4^4}{4!} = 0.1858$ (correct to 4 s.f.)

> Notice the way $e^{-3.4}$ can be taken out as a factor to simplify the calculation.

(ii) $P(X \le 2) = e^{-3.4}\left(1 + 3.4 + \dfrac{3.4^2}{2}\right) = 0.3397$
(correct to 4 s.f.)

(b) $P(4 \le X \le 7) = P(X \le 7) - P(X \le 3)$

$= 0.9769 - 0.5584$

$= 0.4185$ (correct to 4 s.f.)

> The Poisson cumulative distribution function tables are used to look up the $P(X \le x)$ values.

> Here we use the result $E(aX + b) = aE(X) + b$ which needs to be remembered.

③ (a) $E(Y) = E(4X - 2) = 4E(X) - 2$

Now, $E(X) = np = 20 \times 0.25 = 5$,

so, $E(Y) = 4 \times 5 - 2 = 18$.

> The value of $E(X)$ is substituted into the equation $E(Y) = 4E(X) - 2$.

(b) $Var(X) = np(1 - p) = 5(1 - 0.25) = 3.75$

$Var(Y) = Var(4X - 2)$

$= 4^2 Var(X)$

$= 16 \times 3.75$

$= 60$

> Here we use the result $Var(aX + b) = a^2 Var(X)$

(c) When $Y = 10$, $4X - 2 = 10$, giving $X = 3$.

$P(X = 3) = \binom{20}{3}0.25^3(1 - 0.25)^{17}$

$= 0.1339$

Hence, $P(Y = 10) = 0.1339$

> By tables $P(X = 3) = P(X \le 3) - P(X \le 2)$
> $= 0.2252 - 0.0913$
> $= 0.1339$

④ Mean $\lambda = np = 100 \times 0.08 = 8$

X is Po (8)

$P(X < 5) = P(X \le 4) = 0.0996$

> The Poisson distribution function table is used here to find $P(X \le 4)$ with $x = 4$, and mean $\lambda = 8$.

4 Continuous probability distributions

① $E(g(X)) = \int g(x)f(x)dx$

Now $g(x) = \sqrt{x}$

Hence $E(g(X)) = \int_0^1 \sqrt{x}\,f(x)dx$

$$= \int_0^1 \sqrt{x}\left(\tfrac{1}{2}\sqrt{x} + \tfrac{2}{3}\right)dx$$

$$= \int_0^1 \left(\tfrac{1}{2}x + \tfrac{2}{3}x^{\frac{1}{2}}\right)dx$$

$$= \left[\frac{x^2}{4} + \frac{4}{9}x^{\frac{3}{2}}\right]_0^1$$

$$= \left[\left(\frac{1}{4} + \frac{4}{9}\right) - (0)\right]$$

$$= \frac{25}{36} = 0.6944 \text{ (correct to 4 d.p.)}$$

② (a) $\int_{-2}^{2} f(x)dx = 1$

$\int_{-2}^{2} k(4-x)dx = 1$

$k\int_{-2}^{2} (4-x)dx = 1$

$\left[4x - \dfrac{x^2}{2}\right]_{-2}^{2} = 1$

$k[(8-2) - (-8-2)] = 1$

$16k = 1$

$k = \dfrac{1}{16}$

(b) (i) $E(X) = \int xf(x)dx$

$E(X) = \int_{-2}^{2} x\,\tfrac{1}{16}\left(4-x\right)dx$

$$= \frac{1}{16}\int_{-2}^{2} (4x - x^2)dx$$

$$= \frac{1}{16}\left[2x^2 - \frac{x^3}{3}\right]_{-2}^{2}$$

$$= \frac{1}{16}\left[\left(8 - \frac{8}{3}\right) - \left(8 + \frac{8}{3}\right)\right]$$

$$= -\frac{1}{3}$$

> Remember that to integrate you increase the index by 1 and then divide by this new index.

(ii) $P(-1 \le x \le 1) = \int_{-1}^{1} f(x)\,dx$

$$= \int_{-1}^{1} \frac{1}{16}\left(4 - x\right)dx$$

$$= \frac{1}{16}\int_{-1}^{1}\left(4 - x\right)dx$$

$$= \frac{1}{16}\left[4x - \frac{x^2}{2}\right]_{-1}^{1}$$

$$= \frac{1}{16}\left[\left(4 - \frac{1}{2}\right) - \left(-4 - \frac{1}{2}\right)\right]$$

$$= \frac{8}{16} = \frac{1}{2}$$

③   (a) $P(0.25 \le X \le 0.75) = F(0.75) - F(0.25)$

$$= (5 \times 0.75^2 - 4 \times 0.75) - (5 \times 0.25^2 - 4 \times 0.25)$$

$$= 0.5$$

(b) $f(x) = \dfrac{d}{dx}F(x) = \dfrac{d}{dx}\left(5x^2 - 4x\right) = 10x - 4$

(c) $E(X) = \int xf(x)\,dx$

$E(X) = \int_{0}^{1} x(10x - 4)\,dx$

$E(X) = \int_{0}^{1}(10x^2 - 4x)\,dx$

$$= \left[\frac{10x^3}{3} - 2x^2\right]_{0}^{1}$$

$$= \left[\left(\frac{10}{3} - 2\right) - (0 - 0)\right]$$

$$= \frac{4}{3}$$

Appendix

Use of *Statistical Tables* by Murdoch and Barnes

Important note – You only should read this appendix if your school/college uses the following book of statistical tables for the course and in the examination:

Statistical Tables by J Murdoch and JA Barnes (MB) published by Palgrave Macmillan.

Using MB binomial distribution tables to determine probabilities

The Cumulative Binomial Probabilities table in MB gives the probability of r or more successes in a sequence of n independent trials, each of which has a probability of success p.

The table works out the probability for the following function:

$$P(X \geq r) = \sum_{x=r}^{n} \binom{n}{x} p^x (1-p)^{n-x}$$

Note that this function adds up the individual probabilities of obtaining r or more successes.

In the following, we give some examples illustrating the use of MB tables.

Examples

❶ When cuttings of a certain plant are taken, the probability of each cutting rooting is 0.25 independently of all other cuttings.

Joshua takes 20 cuttings. Find the probability of at least 10 of the cuttings taking root.

Answer

① Here we have $n = 20$, $p = 0.25$ and $r = 10$.

Using the tables we obtain a probability for
$P(X \geq 10) = 0.0139$

Here we will use the binomial distribution function table to work out the total probability of 10 or more taking root.

❷ The probability that a machine part fails in its first year is 0.05 independently of all other parts. In a batch of 20 randomly selected parts, find the probability that in the first year:

(a) exactly one part fails

(b) more than 2 parts fail.

Answer

② (a) Using $(X = x) = \binom{n}{x} p^x (1-p)^{n-x}$,

with $x = 1$, $n = 20$ and $p = 0.05$ we obtain
$P(X = 1) = \binom{20}{1} 0.05^1 (1 - 0.05)^{20-1}$

$= \binom{20}{1} 0.05^1 (0.95)^{19}$

$= 0.3773536$

$= 0.3774$ (correct to 4 s.f.)

Note that no method is specified in the question so for the answer you can use the binomial formula or use the tables.

Alternative method using tables with $n = 20$ and $p = 0.05$ we have

$P(X = 1) = P(X \geq 1) - P(X \geq 2)$

$= 0.6415 - 0.2642$

$= 0.3773$

(b) $P(X > 2) = P(X \geq 3) = 0.0755$

> Note that the tables give a cumulative probability, so if we want the probability of 1 only we need to subtract the probabilities of X being greater than or equal to 1 and subtract the probability of X being greater than or equal to 2.

> Note the slight difference in the answers between the calculated probability and the probability found using tables. This is caused by rounding off in the tables.

> Tables have been used here but the binomial formula could also be used.

What to do if $p > 0.50$, as the tables do not show values above $p = 0.50$

It should be noted that in the tables for the binomial distribution the highest value of p considered is 0.50. When dealing with binomial distributions in which $p > 0.5$, we note that the probability of a failure $q = 1 - p < 0.5$. In this case, we consider the number of failures instead of the number of successes.

Examples

❶ Given that X has the binomial distribution B (10, 0.6), find the values of:

(a) $P(X = 8)$

(b) $P(6 \leq X \leq 10)$

Answer

① Let $Y = 10 - X$

> X is the number of successes.
> Y is the number of failures.

Then Y has the distribution B (10, 0.4)

(a) $P(X = 8) = P(Y = 2) = P(Y \geq 2) - P(Y \geq 3)$

$= 0.9536 - 0.8327$

$= 0.1209$

(b) $P(6 \leq X \leq 10) = P(0 \leq Y \leq 4)$

$= P(Y \geq 0) - P(Y \geq 5)$

$= 1 - 0.3669$

$= 0.6331$

❷ The probability that a randomly chosen daffodil bulb will produce a flower is 0.8. If 20 such bulbs are planted, find the probabilities that:

(a) exactly 12 of them will produce flowers

(b) fewer than 8 will produce flowers.

Answer

②(a)   Let X be the number of bulbs that produce flowers, so that X is distributed as B (20, 0.8).

Since $p = 0.8 > 0.5$ we consider $Y = 20 - X$ and note that Y is distributed as B (20, 0.2).

$$P(X = 12) = P(Y = 8)$$

$$= P(Y \geq 8) - P(Y \geq 9)$$

$$= 0.0321 - 0.0100$$

$$= 0.0221$$

> X is the number of successes.
>
> Y is the number of failures.

(b) $P(X < 8) = P(X \leq 7) = P(Y \geq 13)$

$$= 0$$

> Note that there is no entry for the particular pair of values $r = 13$ and $p = 0.20$ for the value of $n = 20$, this shows that the probability is very near to zero (i.e. less than 0.00005).

The Poisson distribution

The following example shows how the *Statistical Tables* by Murdoch and Barnes can be used to solve a problem involving the Poisson distribution. Note that no method is included in the question, which means that the formula could also be used to solve this problem. The method using the formula can be seen in the topic on page 53.

Example

❶   Use the random variable $X \sim$ Po (1.4) to determine

(a) $P(X = 2)$

(b) $P(X \geq 1)$

(c) $P(2 < X \leq 4)$

Answer

①   (a) $P(X = 2) = P(X \geq 2) - P(X \geq 3) = 0.4082 - 0.1665 = 0.2417$

(b) $P(X \geq 1) = 0.7534$

(c) $P(2 < X \leq 4) = P(X \geq 3) - P(X \geq 5)$

$$= 0.1665 - 0.0143 = 0.1522$$

Using the Poisson distribution to approximate the binomial distribution

Both the binomial and Poisson distributions are discrete probability distributions.

In general we can approximate the binomial distribution by using the Poisson distribution in the following circumstances:

If n is large (usually > 50) and

p is small (usually <0.1).

In the above circumstances B(n, p) can be approximated by Po(λ) where $\lambda = np$.

> **≫ Grade boost**
>
> Do not get these mixed up with the conditions needed to be able to use the binomial distribution to solve a problem.

Mean and variance of the Poisson distribution

There are formulae for the mean and variance of a Poisson distribution.

If X is Po (λ) then, Mean, $m = \lambda$, Variance $= m = \lambda$.

Using Poisson distribution function tables to work out $P(X \geq r)$

Poisson distribution function tables can be used to work out $P(X \geq r)$. For example, if you wanted to find $P(X \geq 3)$ for a distribution Po (0.8) you would look up the intersection of the row where $r = 3$ with the column where λ or $m = 0.8$ to give the required probability of 0.0474.

❶ Given that 5% of pupils in a school are left-handed, use the Poisson distribution to estimate the probability that a random sample of 100 pupils in the school contains two or more left-handed pupils.

Answer

① $m = np = 100 \times 0.05 = 5$

X is approximately distributed as Po(5)

$P(X \geq 2) = 0.9596$

❷ The random variable X has the binomial distribution B (300, 0.012). Use a Poisson approximation to find an approximate value for the probability that X is less than 3.

Answer

② Mean $= np = 300 \times 0.012 = 3.6$

X is approximately distributed as Po (3.6)   (i.e. $X \sim$ Po(3.6))

$P(X < 3) = 1 - P(X \geq 3)$

$\qquad = 1 - 0.6973$

$\qquad = 0.3027$

> Compare B (300, 0.012) with B (n, p) gives $n = 300$ and $p = 0.012$.

> Note that this means $m = 3.6$.

❸ Cars arrive at a petrol station in such a way that the number arriving during an interval of length t minutes has a Poisson distribution with mean $0.2t$.

(a) Find the probability that:

   (i)   exactly ten cars arrive between 9 a.m. and 10 a.m.

   (ii) more than five cars arrive between 11 a.m. and 11.30 a.m.   [6]

(b) The probability that no cars arrive during an interval of length t minutes is equal to 0·03. Without the use of tables, find the value of t.   [4]

(WJEC S1 June 2011 Q4)

Answer

③ (a) (i) Mean $m = \lambda = 0.2t$ and over 60 min (i.e. 1 hr) $\lambda = 0.2 \times 60 = 12$

X is distributed as Po(12)

$P(X = 10) = e^{-12} \dfrac{12^{10}}{10!} = 0.1048$ (correct to 4 s.f.)

   (ii) Mean $\lambda = 0.2t$ and over 30 min (i.e. 0.5 hr) $\lambda = 0.2 \times 30 = 6$

X is Po(6)

$P(X > 5) = P(X \geq 6) = 0.5543$ (correct to 4 s.f.)

> Note that $P(X \geq 6)$ is found by using tables.

(b) Mean $\lambda = 0.2t$

$P(X = 0) = e^{-0.2t}\dfrac{(0.2t)^0}{0!}$

$P(X = 0) = e^{-0.2t}$

Now, $P(X = 0) = 0.03$

Hence, $e^{-0.2t} = 0.03$

Taking $\log_e$ of both sides, we obtain

$-0.2t = \log_e 0.03$

Solving, gives $t = 17.5$ min (correct to one decimal place).

> Note that $(0.2t)^0 = 1$ and also that $0! = 1$.

> Note that the solving of equations by the use of logarithms were covered in Core 2. Instead of taking $\log_e$ of both sides you could have used $\log_{10}$.

Examination style questions

We give here the alternative solution to examination question 3 on page 58.

3 On a turtle farm, turtles are bred and hatched from eggs under controlled conditions.

(a) The probability of producing a female turtle from an egg is 0.4 under the controlled conditions. The probability of producing a female from an egg is independent of other eggs hatching to produce female turtles. When 20 eggs are kept under the controlled conditions, find the probability that:

  (i) exactly 10 female turtles are produced

  (ii) more than 7 female turtles are produced. [5]

(b) During the hatching process, the probability that an egg fails to hatch is 0.05. When 300 eggs are kept under the controlled conditions, use the Poisson approximation to find the probability that the number of eggs failing to hatch is less than 10. [3]

Answer

③ (a) (i) $P(X = x) = \binom{n}{x}p^x(1 - p)^{n-x}$

$p = 0.4, n = 20$ and $x = 10$.

$P(X = 10) = \binom{20}{10}0.4^{10}(1 - 0.4)^{20-10}$

$P(X = 10) = \binom{20}{10}0.4^{10}(0.6)^{10}$

$= 0.1171$ (correct to 4 s.f.)

(ii) $P(X > 7) = P(X \geq 8)$

$= 0.5841$

(b) $m = np = 300 \times 0.05 = 15$

X is distributed as Po(15)

$P(X < 10) = 1 - P(X \geq 10) = 1 - 0.9301 = 0.0699$

> $P(X = 10) = P(X \geq 10) - P(X \geq 11)$
> $= 0.7576 - 0.6528$
> $= 0.1048$

> The binomial distribution B(20, 0.4) is used here. The probability $p = 0.4$ is too high for the Poisson distribution to be used where ideally p should be less than 0.1. Also, n should be > 50.

> Tables should be used here as using the formula would be tedious because you would have 10 individual probabilities to calculate before adding them together.

Q&A 1

1   (a)   A series of trials is carried out, each resulting in either success or failure. State **two** conditions that have to be satisfied in order for the total number of successes to be modelled by the binomial distribution. [2]

   (b)   Each time Ann shoots an arrow at a target, she hits it with probability 0·4. She shoots 20 arrows at the target. Determine the probability that she hits it:

      (i)   exactly 8 times

      (ii) between 6 and 10 times (both inclusive). [5]

   (c)   Each time she shoots an arrow, she hits the centre of the target with probability 0·04. She shoots 100 arrows at the target. Use a Poisson approximation to find the probability that she hits the centre of the target fewer than 5 times. [3]

(WJEC S1 June 2011 Q7)

Answer

1   (a)   The two conditions are:

   ▪ independent trials,

   ▪ trials where there is a constant probability of success.

   Grade boost

   Questions on the conditions for which a certain modelling formula can be used are frequent. Make sure you remember the conditions for each formula you use.

   (b)   (i) $P(X = x) = \binom{n}{x}p^x(1 - p)^{n-x}$

      Now $p = 0.4, n = 20, x = 8$, so we have

      $P(X = 8) = \binom{20}{8}0.4^8(1 - 0.4)^{20-8}$

      $P(X = 8) = \binom{20}{8}0.4^8(0.6)^{12}$

            $= 0.1787$ (correct to 4 s.f.)

   The formula is obtained from the formula booklet.

   $P(X = 8) = P(X \geq 8) - P(X \geq 9)$

         $= 0.5841 - 0.4044$

         $= 0.1797$ (correct to 4 s.f.)

      (ii) $P(6 \leq X \leq 10) = P(X \geq 6) - P(X \geq 11)$

               $= 0.8744 - 0.1275$

               $= 0.7469$ (correct to 4 s.f.)

   (c)   Mean, $m = np = 100 \times 0.04 = 4$

      The number of hits, X, is approximately Po(4).

      $P(X < 5) = 1 - P(X \geq 5) = 1 - 0.3712 = 0.6288$ (correct to 4 s.f.)

   The Poisson distribution function tables are used to look up the $P(X \geq x)$ values. Using the tables the probability corresponding to values $r = 4$ and $m = 4$ is looked up.

Q&A 2

2   Wine glasses are packed in boxes, each containing 20 glasses. Each glass has a probability of 0·05 of being broken in transit, independently of all other glasses.

   (a)   Let X denote the number of glasses in a box broken in transit.

      (i)   State the distribution of X.

      (ii) **Without** the use of tables, calculate $P(X = 1)$.

      (iii) **Using tables**, determine the value of $P(X = 3)$. [5]

(b) A retailer buys 10 of these boxes. Use a Poisson approximation to find the probability that fewer than 5 of the 200 glasses are broken in transit. [3]

(WJEC S1 Jan 2011 Q8)

Answer

2 (a) (i) The distribution is B (20, 0.05)

(ii) $P(X = 1) = \binom{20}{1}0.05^1(1 - 0.05)^{20 - 1}$

$= \binom{20}{1}0.05^1(0.95)^{19}$

$= 0.377$ (correct to 3 s.f.)

> This is a Binomial distribution because n is small and would need to be >50 to use the Poisson distribution. Hence we insert $n = 20$ and $p = 0.05$ into B (n, p) to give B (20, 0.05).

> Use the formula $P(X = x) = \binom{n}{x}p^x(1 - p)^{n - x}$ obtained from the formula booklet.

(iii) $P(X \geq 3) = 0.0755$

> Use the Binomial cumulative distribution table to find $P(X \geq 3)$.
> Use the table with $n = 20$, $p = 0.05$ and $r = 3$.

(b) Mean $m = np = 200 \times 0.05 = 10$

X is Po(10)

$P(X < 5) = P(X \leq 4) = 1 - P(X \geq 5) = 1 - 0.9707 = 0.0293$

Q&A3

3 When seeds of a certain variety of flower are planted, the probability of each seed germinating is 0·8, independently of all other seeds.

(a) David plants 20 of these seeds. Find the probability that:

(i) exactly 15 seeds germinate

(ii) at least 15 seeds germinate. [6]

(b) Beti plants n of these seeds and she correctly calculates that the probability that they all germinate is 0.10737, correct to five decimal places. Find the value of n. [3]

(WJEC S1 Jan 2010 Q5)

Answer

3 (a) (i) Distribution is B(20, 0.8)

$P(X = 15) = \binom{20}{15}0.8^{15}(1 - 0.8)^5$

$= 0.1746$

> Or Let Y = no of seeds failing to germinate.
> Y is distributed as B(20, 0.2)
> $P(X = 15) = P(Y = 5)$
> $= P(Y \geq 5) - P(Y \geq 6)$
> $= 0.3704 - 0.1958 = 0.1746$

(ii) Let the number of seeds failing to germinate = Y.

Y is distributed as B(20, 0.2)

> Use the Binomial cumulative distribution function table with $n = 20$, $p = 0.2$ and $r = 6$. Read off the probability which is 0.1958.

$$P(X \geq 15) = P(Y \leq 5) = 1 - P(Y \geq 6) = 1 - 0.1958 = 0.8042$$

(b) Distribution is B(n, 0.8)

$$P(X = n) = \binom{n}{n}0.8^n(1 - 0.8)^0$$

$0.10737 = 0.8^n$

Taking $\log_e$ of both sides, we obtain

> Note that you could also take logarithms of both sides to base 10 to solve this equation.

$\log_e 0.10737 = \log_e 0.8^n$

so $\log_e 0.10737 = n \log_e 0.8$

$$n = \frac{\log_e 0.10737}{\log_e 0.8}$$

> Note that as n is the number of seeds germinating, n has to be an integer.

Hence, $n = 10$

Test yourself (using MB Tables)

1 It is known that 25% of the bulbs in a box produce yellow flowers. A customer buys 20 of these bulbs. Find the probability that:

(a) exactly 4 bulbs produce yellow flowers

(b) fewer than 8 bulbs produce yellow flowers.

2 The number of items of junk mail arriving by post each day at a house can be modelled by a Poisson distribution with mean 3.4.

(a) Without using tables, calculate:

    (i) $P(X = 4)$

    (ii) $P(X \leq 2)$.

(b) Using tables, determine

    $P(4 \leq X \leq 7)$.

3 The random variable X has the binomial distribution B (20, 0.25).

Given that $Y = 4X - 2$, calculate

(a) $E(Y)$,

(b) $Var(Y)$,

(c) $P(Y = 10)$.

4 Each time a dart player throws a dart at the bulls-eye they hit the bulls-eye with a probability 0.08. The dart player throws 100 darts at the bulls-eye. Use a Poisson approximation to find the probability that she hits the bulls-eye fewer than 5 times.

Test yourself answers

3 Binomial and Poisson distributions (MB Tables)

① (a) $P(X = x) = \binom{n}{x} p^x (1 - p)^{n-x}$

  $p = 0.25$ and $n = 20$.

  $P(X = 4) = \binom{20}{4} 0.25^4 (1 - 0.25)^{20-4}$

  $\qquad = \binom{20}{4} 0.25^4 (0.75)^{16}$

  $\qquad = 0.1897$ (correct to 4 s.f.)

> By tables $P(X = 4) = P(X \geq 4) - P(X \geq 5)$
> $\qquad = 0.77488 - 0.5852 = 0.1896$

  (b) The binomial distribution tables are used here with $n = 20, p = 0.25$ and $r = 7$.

  P(fewer than 8 bulbs) $= P(X \leq 7) = 1 - P(X \geq 8) = 1 - 0.1018 = 0.8982$

② (a) (i) $P(X = 4) = e^{-3.4} \dfrac{3.4^4}{4!} = 0.1858$ (correct to 4 s.f.)

> Notice the way $e^{-3.4}$ can be taken out as a factor to simplify the calculation.

   (ii) $P(X \leq 2) = e^{-3.4} \left(1 + 3.4 + \dfrac{3.4^2}{2} \right) = 0.3397$
   (correct to 4 s.f.)

  (b) $P(4 \leq X \leq 7) = P(X \geq 4) - P(X \geq 8)$

  $\qquad = 0.4416 - 0.0231$

> The Poisson Cumulative Distribution Function tables are used to look up the $P(X \geq r)$ values.

  $\qquad = 0.4185$ (correct to 4 s.f.)

③ (a) $E(Y) = E(4X - 2) = 4E(X) - 2$

  Now, $E(X) = np = 20 \times 0.25 = 5$,

  so, $E(Y) = 4 \times 5 - 2 = 18$.

> The value of $E(X)$ is substituted into the equation $E(Y) = 4E(X) - 2$.

  (b) $Var(X) = np(1 - p) = 5(1 - 0.25) = 3.75$

  $Var(Y) = Var(4X - 2)$

  $\qquad = 4^2 \, Var(X)$

  $\qquad = 16 \times 3.75$

  $\qquad = 60$

> Here we use the result
> $Var\,(aX + b) = a^2 \, Var(X)$

  (c) When $Y = 10$, $4X - 2 = 10$, giving $X = 3$.

  $P(X = 3) = \binom{20}{3} 0.25^3 (1 - 0.25)^{17}$

  $\qquad = 0.1339$

> By tables $P(X = 3) = P(X \geq 3) - P(X \geq 4)$
> $\qquad = 0.9087 - 0.7748$
> $\qquad = 0.1339$

  Hence, $P(Y = 10) = 0.1339$

④ Mean $\quad m = \lambda = np = 100 \times 0.08 = 8$

  X is Po (8)

  $P(X < 5) = 1 - P(X \geq 5) = 1 - 0.9004 = 0.0996$

> The Poisson distribution function table is used here to find $P(X \geq 5)$ with $r = 5$, and mean $m = 8$.

Summary: Binomial and Poisson distributions

See page 63.